all time FAVORITE hymNS

COMPILED BY
JIMMIE DAVIS

A Collection of Gospel Songs and
Hymns, Practical and Inspiring,
for Religious Services of all
Kinds, Conventions, Singings,
also, Radio and Television . . .

Special prices to churches

JIMMIE DAVIS MUSIC CO., Inc.

836 Rutherford Street
Shreveport, Louisiana

★

Foreword and Dedication . . .

The wonderful hymns of other days have been a great inspiration to millions of people everywhere and it is our wish that they be preserved and that all people will be encouraged to use them even more. In this book you will find songs that have inspired many men. For God speaks in many ways, and so often in song. These old songs that have survived through the ages have been appealingly strong in both words and music. To these selections we have added the greatest hymns and gospel songs of the modern age that we feel will also be a deep inspiration to people everywhere.

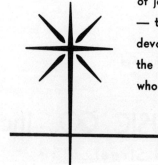

To all of those whose redeemed hearts are full of joy and testimony in song — to the singers — to the gospel quartets, and the choirs who devote a big part of their lives to transmitting the message through song, and to all of those who listen, — this book is dedicated.

Someone To Care

J. D.   Slowly with feeling   Jimmie Davis

1. When the world seems cold and your friends seem few, There is someone who
2. When your dis-appointments come and you feel so blue, There is someone who

cares for you; When you've tears in your eyes, your heart bleeds inside, There is
cares for you; When you need a friend, a friend till the end, There is

CHORUS

someone who cares for you.   Some-one to care, Someone to share
someone who's a friend to you.

all your trou-bles like no oth-er can do;   He'll come down from the

skies and brush the tears from your eyes, You're His child and He cares for you.

There Is Power In The Blood

I Am Thine, O Lord

3

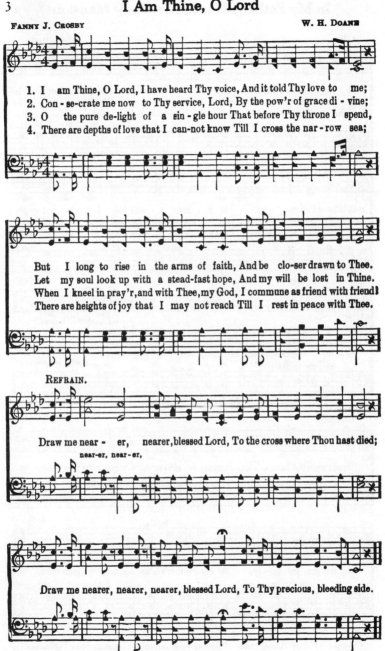

FANNY J. CROSBY

W. H. DOANE

1. I am Thine, O Lord, I have heard Thy voice, And it told Thy love to me;
2. Con - se-crate me now to Thy service, Lord, By the pow'r of grace di - vine;
3. O the pure de-light of a sin - gle hour That before Thy throne I spend,
4. There are depths of love that I can-not know Till I cross the nar - row sea;

But I long to rise in the arms of faith, And be clo-ser drawn to Thee.
Let my soul look up with a stead-fast hope, And my will be lost in Thine.
When I kneel in pray'r, and with Thee, my God, I commune as friend with friend!
There are heights of joy that I may not reach Till I rest in peace with Thee.

REFRAIN.

Draw me near - er, nearer, blessed Lord, To the cross where Thou hast died;

near-er, near-er,

Draw me nearer, nearer, nearer, blessed Lord, To Thy precious, bleeding side.

In My Father's House Are Many Mansions

A. H.

Aileene Hanks

1. In my Father's house are man - y mansions, If it were not true He
2. Je - sus died up - on the cross to bear my sor- row, Freely died that souls like
3. When your friends have turned you down and left you lone- ly, In this world you're all a-

would have told me so; He has gone a - way to live in that bright
you might have new life; But I know there soon will come a bright to-
lone and O so blue; Turn your tho'ts a - way from sin to Je - sus

FINE

cit - y, He's pre - par - ing me a man-sion there I know.
mor-row, When the world will all be free from sin and strife.
on - ly, A new life and friendship sweet He'll give to you.

D. S.-If you're true then to this land you'll sure- ly go.

CHORUS

Do not shun the Saviour's love, from up in glo - ry, Or you won't be there to

D. S.

sing the gos - pel sto - ry; In my Fa-ther's house are man - y man-sions,

He Washed My Eyes With Tears

I. S.

Ira Stanphill

With Feeling

1. He washed my eyes with tears that I might see, The broken heart I had
2. He washed my eyes with tears that I might see, The glo-ry of Him-self

was good for me; He tore it all a - part and looked in - side, He found
re-vealed to me; I did not know that He had wounded hands, I saw

it full of fear and fool-ish pride. He swept a - way the things that made
the blood He spilt up - on the sands. I saw the marks of shame and wept

me blind, And then I saw the clouds were sil - ver lined; And now I un-der-
and cried, He was my sub-sti-tute for me He died; And now I'm glad He

stand 'twas best for me, He washed my eyes with tears that I might see.
came so ten-der - ly, And washed my eyes with tears that I might see.

Love Lifted Me

6

James Rowe

Howard E. Smith

1. I was sink-ing deep in sin, Far from the peaceful shore, Ver-y deep-ly stained with-in, Sink-ing to rise no more; But the Mas-ter of the sea Heard my de-spair-ing cry, From the wa-ters lift-ed me, Now safe am I.

2. All my heart to Him I give, Ev-er to Him I'll cling, In His bless-ed pres-ence live, Ev-er His prais-es sing; Love so might-y and so true Mer-its my soul's best songs, Faith-ful, lov-ing serv-ice, too, To Him be-longs.

3. Souls in dan-ger, look a-bove, Je-sus complete-ly saves, He will lift you by His love Out of the an-gry waves; He's the Mas-ter of the sea, Bil-lows His will o-bey; He your Sav-iour wants to be—Be saved to-day.

CHORUS

Love lift-ed me! Love lift-ed me!
e-ven me! e-ven me!
When noth-ing else could help, Love lift-ed me. Love lift-ed me.

Wasted Years

W. F.   Wally Fowler

1. Have you wandered a-long on life's pathway, Have you lived with-out love, a
2. Search for wis-dom and seek un-der-stand-ing, There is someone who knows and

life of tears;   Have you searched for the great   hid-den meaning,   Or
al-ways hears;   Give it up! Give it up! the load you're bearing   You

CHORUS

is your life filled with long   wast-ed years.   Wast-ed years, wasted years, Oh how
can't go on in a   life of wast-ed years.

fool-ish,   As you walk on   in dark-ness and fears;   Turn around, turn

a-round, God is call-ing,   He's calling you from a   life of wasted years.

The Old Rugged Cross

G. B.   Solo and Chorus   Rev. Geo. Bennard

1. On a hill far a-way stood an old rug-ged cross, The emblem of
2. Oh, that old rug-ged cross, so despised by the world, Has a wondrous at-
3. In the old rug-ged cross, stained with blood so di-vine, A won-drous
4. To the old rug-ged cross, I will ev-er be true, Its shame and re-

suf-f'ring and shame, And I love that old cross where the dear-est and best
trac-tion for me, For the dear Lamb of God left His glo-ry a-bove,
beau-ty I see; For 'twas on that old cross Je-sus suf-fered and died,
proach glad-ly bear; Then He'll call me some day to my home far a-way,

CHORUS

For a world of lost sin-ners was slain. So I'll cher-ish the old rug-ged
To bear it to dark Cal-va-ry.
To par-don and sanc-ti-fy me.
Where His glo-ry for-ev-er I'll share. cross, the

cross,......... Till my trophies at last I lay down; I will cling to the
old rug-ged cross,

old rug-ged cross,......... And exchange it some day for a crown.
cross, the old rug-ged cross,

9

The Last Mile Of The Way

Rev. Johnson Oatman, Jr.   Wm. Edie Marks

1. If   I   walk in   the pathway of du - ty,   If   I   work till the
2. If   for Christ I proclaim the glad sto - ry,   If   I   seek for His
3. Here the dear - est of ties we must sev - er, Tears of sor - row are
4. And if here I have earn-est - ly striv - en, And have tried all His

close of the day;   I shall see the great King in His beau - ty,
sheep gone a - stray,   I am sure He will show me His glo - ry,
seen ev - 'ry day;   But no sick-ness, no sigh - ing for - ev - er
will   to o - bey, 'Twill en-hance all the rap - ture of heav - en,

FINE   CHORUS

When I've gone the last mile of the way.   When I've gone the last

D. S.-When I've gone the last mile of the way.

mile of the way, ...   I will rest at the close of the
the   last mile of the way,   at the

D. S.

day, ...And I know there are joys that a - wait me,
close of the day,

Jesus Saves

Priscilla J. Owens

Wm. J. Kirkpatrick

1. We have heard the joy - ful sound: Je - sus saves! Je - sus saves!
2. Waft it on the roll - ing tide; Je - sus saves! Je - sus saves!
3. Sing a - bove the bat - tle strife, Je - sus saves! Je - sus saves!
4. Give the winds a might - y voice, Je - sus saves! Je - sus saves!

Spread the ti - dings all a - round: Je - sus saves! Je - sus saves!
Tell to sin - ners far and wide: Je - sus saves! Je - sus saves!
By His death and end - less life, Je - sus saves! Je - sus saves!
Let the na - tions now re - joice, Je - sus saves! Je - sus saves!

Bear the news to ev - 'ry land, Climb the steeps and cross the waves;
Sing, ye is - lands of the sea, Ech - o back, ye o - cean caves;
Sing it soft - ly thru the gloom, When the heart for mer - cy craves;
Shout sal - va - tion full and free, High - est hills and deep - est caves;

On - ward! 'tis our Lord's com - mand; Je - sus saves! Je - sus saves!
Earth shall keep her ju - bi - lee; Je - sus saves! Je - sus saves!
Sing in tri - umph o'er the tomb; Je - sus saves! Je - sus saves!
This our song of vic - to - ry; Je - sus saves! Je - sus saves!

There Shall Be Showers Of Blessing

El Nathan   James McGranahan

1. "There shall be show-ers of bless-ing" This is the prom-ise of love;
2. "There shall be show-ers of bless-ing" Pre-cious, re-viv-ing a-gain,
3. "There shall be show-ers of bless-ing" Send them up-on us, O Lord!
4. "There shall be show-ers of bless-ing" O that to-day they might fall,

There shall be sea-sons re-fresh-ing, Sent from the Sav-ior a-bove.
O-ver the hills and the val-leys Sound of a-bun-dance of rain.
Grant to us now a re-fresh-ing, Come, and now hon-or Thy Word!
Now as to God we're con-fess-ing, Now as on Je-sus we call!

CHORUS

Show - ers of bless-ing, Showers of bless-ing we need;
Show - ers, show-ers

Mer-cy-drops round us are fall-ing, But for the show-ers we plead.

Born To Serve The Lord

B. C.

Bud Chambers

1. From the dust of the earth God cre - a - ted man, His breath
2. My hands were made to help my neigh - bor, My eyes

made man a liv-ing soul; And God so loved the world He
were made to read God's word; My feet were made to

gave His on - ly Son, And that is why I love Him so.
walk in His foot-steps, My bod - y is the temple of the Lord.

CHORUS

I was made in His like-ness, Cre - a - ted in His im - age, For I

was born to serve the Lord; And I can't de - ny Him, I'll al - ways

Born To Serve The Lord

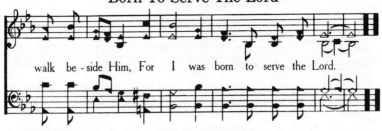

walk be-side Him, For I was born to serve the Lord.

13   Near To The Heart Of·God

Cleland B. McAfee   Cleland B. McAfee

1. There is a place of qui-et rest, Near to the heart of God,
2. There is a place of comfort sweet, Near to the heart of God,
3. There is a place of full re-lease, Near to the heart of God,

A place where sin can-not mo-lest, Near to the heart of God.
A place where we our Sav-ior meet, Near to the heart of God.
A place where all is joy and peace, Near to the heart of God.

REFRAIN

O Je-sus, blest Re-deem-er, Sent from the heart of God,

Hold us, who wait be-fore Thee, Near to the heart of God.

Supper Time

Ira Stanphill

Duet Soprano (or Tenor) and Alto.

1. When I was but a boy in days of child-hood I used to play till
2. One day be-side her bed-side I was kneel-ing And an-gel wings were
3. In vi-sions now I see her stand-ing yon-der And her fa-mil-iar

eve-ning shad-ows come Then wind-ing down an old fa-mil-iar path-
win-now-ing the air She heard the call for Sup-per Time in heav-
voice I hear once more, The ban-quet ta-ble's read-y up in heav-

CHORUS

way I heard my moth-er call at set of sun. Come home, come
en And now I know she's wait-ing for me there.
en It's sup-per time up-on the gold-en strand.

home it's sup-per time, The shad-ows length in fast, Come home, come

home it's sup-per time: We're go-ing home at last.

Send The Light

C. H. G.

Chas. H. Gabriel

1. There's a call comes ring-ing o'er the rest-less wave, Send the light!
2. We have heard the Ma - ce - don - ian call to-day,
3. We will not grow wea - ry in the work of love, Send the light!

send the light! There are souls to res - cue, there are
And a gold - en of - f'ring at the
send the light! Let us gath - er jew - els for a

souls to save, Send the light! send the light!
cross we lay,
crown a - bove, Send the light! send the light!

CHORUS

Send the light! the bless-ed gos - pel light, Let it
Send the light! the bless-ed gos - pel light,

shine from shore to shore! for-ev - er-more.
Let it shine from shore to shore! for-ev-er-more.

Standing On The Promises

R. K. C.

R. Kelso Carter

1. Stand-ing on the prom-is - es of Christ my King, Thru e - ter - nal
2. Stand-ing on the prom-is - es that can - not fail, When the howl-ing
3. Stand-ing on the prom-is - es I now can see, Per-fect, pre-sent
4. Stand-ing on the prom-is - es of Christ the Lord, Bound to Him e-
5. Stand-ing on the prom-is - es, I can-not fall, List'n-ing ev - 'ry

a - ges let His praises ring, Glo-ry in the high-est, I will shout and sing,
storms of doubt and fear as-sail, By the liv-ing Word of God I shall pre-vail
cleansing in the blood for me; Standing in the lib - er - ty where Christ makes free,
ter - nal-ly by love's strong cord, Overcoming dai - ly with the Spir-it's sword,
mo-ment to the Spir-it's call, Rest-ing in my Sav-ior, as my all in all,

CHORUS

Standing on the promis - es of God. Stand - ing, stand - ing,
Standing on the promises, standing on the promises,

Standing on the prom-is- es of God, my Sav-ior, Stand - ing,
Standing on the prom-is - es,

stand - ing, I'm stand-ing on the prom-is - es of God.
standing on the prom-is - es,

17 The Love Of God

F. M. L.

F. M. Lehman
Arr. by Claudia Lehman Mays

1. The love of God is great-er far Than tongue or pen can ev-er tell;
2. When hoar-y time shall pass a-way, And earth-ly thrones and kingdoms fall;
3. Could we with ink the o-cean fill, And were the skies of parchment made;

It goes be-yond the high-est star, And reach-es to the low-est hell.
When men who here re-fuse to pray, On rocks and hill and mountains call;
Were ev-'ry stalk on earth a quill, And ev-'ry man a scribe by trade;

The guilt-y pair, bowed down with care, God gave His Son to win;
God's love, so sure, shall still en-dure, All meas-ure-less and strong;
To write the love of God a-bove Would drain the o-cean dry;

His err-ing child He rec-on-ciled, And par-doned from his sin.
Re-deem-ing grace to Ad-am's race The saints' and an-gels' song.
Nor could the scroll con-tain the whole, Tho' stretched from sky to sky.

CHORUS

Oh, love of God, how rich and pure! How meas-ure-less and strong!
It shall for-ev-er-more en-dure The saints and an-(Omit) gels' song.

I Need No Mansion Here

Words and Music by C. S. Grogan

1. When bur-dens come so hard to bear, That no earth-ly friend can
2. Oh, the tho't to me is sweet, That my loved ones I will
3. When Je-sus comes to claim His own, I will move to my new

share; Tears drive a-way the smiles and leave my heart in pain.
meet; At the end-ing of the jour-ney here be-low.
home; I'll walk and talk with Him up-on the streets of gold.

Then my Lord from heav'n a-bove, Speaks to me in tones of
Seems I hear their voic-es blend, In a world with-out an
A man-sion there is wait-ing me, Soon its beau-ty I will

love; Wipes the tears a-way and makes me smile a-gain.
end; I won't wor-ry when the time shall come to go.
see; In that cit-y where we nev-er shall grow old.

CHORUS

I need no man-sion here be-low, For Je-sus said, "That I could

I Need No Mansion Here

go; To a home be - yond the clouds not made with hands."

Won't you come and go a - long? We will sing the sweet - est

song, Ev - er played up - on the harps in glo - ry land.

19   Where Could I Go

J. B. C.   J. B. Coats

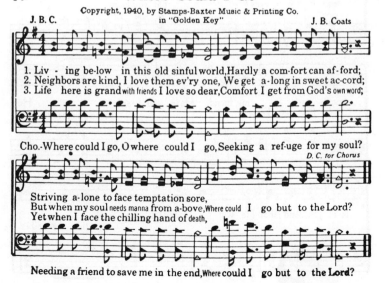

1. Liv - ing be-low in this old sinful world, Hardly a com-fort can af-ford;
2. Neighbors are kind, I love them ev'ry one, We get a-long in sweet ac-cord;
3. Life here is grand with friends I love so dear, Comfort I get from God's own word;

Cho.- Where could I go, O where could I go, Seeking a ref-uge for my soul?

D. C. for Chorus

Striving a-lone to face temptation sore,
But when my soul needs manna from a-bove, Where could I go but to the Lord?
Yet when I face the chilling hand of death,

Needing a friend to save me in the end, Where could I go but to the Lord?

Do You Know My Jesus?

W. F. (Bill) Lakey
and V. B. (Vep) Ellis

1. Have you a heart that's wea-ry, Tend-ing a load of care; Are you a soul that's seek-ing Rest from the bur-den you bear?
2. Where is your heart, oh, pil-grim, What does your light re-veal; Who hears your call for com-fort When naught but sor-row you feel?
3. Who knows your dis-ap-point-ments, Who hears each time you cry; Who un-der-stands your heart-aches, Who dries the tears from your eyes?

CHORUS

Do you know my Je-sus, Do you know my friend, Have you heard He loves you, And that He will a-bide till the end?

That Glad Reunion Day

21

A. M. P.

Adger M. Pace

1. There will be a hap-py meet-ing in heav-en I know,
2. There with-in the ho-ly cit-y we'll sing and re-joice,
3. When we live a mil-lion years in that won-der-ful place,

When we see the man-y loved ones we've known here be-low;
Prais-ing Christ the bless-ed Sav-iour with heart and with voice;
Bask-ing in the love of Je-sus, be-hold-ing His face;

Gath-er on the bless-ed hill-tops with hearts all a-glow,
Tell Him how we came to love Him and make Him our choice,
It will seem but just a mo-ment of prais-ing His grace,

D. S. There with all the ho-ly an-gels and loved ones to stay,

FINE

CHORUS

That will be a glad re-un-ion day. Glad day, a
That will be a hap-py day, yes, a

That will be a glad re-un-ion day.

D. S.

won-der-ful day, Glad day, a glo-ri-ous day;
won-der-ful day, That will be a hap-py day, yes, a glo-ri-ous day;

22

"Whosoever" Meaneth Me

J. E. M.   J. Edwin McConnell

1. I am hap-py to-day and the sun shines bright, The clouds have been
2. All my hopes have been raised, O His name be praised, His glo-ry has
3. O what won-der-ful love, O what grace di-vine, That Je-sus should

rolled a-way; For the Sav-ior said Who-so-ev-er will, May
filled my soul; I've been lift-ed up and from sin set free, His
die for me; I was lost in sin, for the world I pined, But

CHORUS

come with Him to stay. (to stay.)
blood hath made me whole. (me whole.) "Whoso-ev-er," sure-ly mean-eth me,
now I am set free. (set free.)

Sure-ly mean-eth me, O sure-ly mean-eth me; "Who-so-ev-er,"

sure-ly mean-eth me, "Who-so-ev-er," mean-eth me.
mean-eth me.

Room At The Cross For You

Words and Music by Ira Stanphill

1. The cross up-on which Jesus died Is a shel-ter in which we can hide, And its grace so free is suf-fi-cient for me, And deep is its foun-tain; as wide as the sea.

2. Tho' mil-lions have found Him a friend And have turned from the sins they have sinned, The Sav-iour still waits to o-pen the gates, And wel-come a sin-ner be-fore it's too late.

3. The hand of my Sav-iour is strong And the love of my Sav-iour is long, Thro' sun-shine or rain thro' loss or in gain, The blood flows from Cal-v'ry to cleanse ev-'ry stain.

CHORUS

There's room at the cross for you, There's room at the cross for you, Tho' millions have come There's still room for one, Yes, there's room at the cross for you.

What A Day That Will Be

J. H.   Jim Hill

1. There is com-ing a day when no heart - aches shall come, No more
2. There'll be no sor-row there, no more bur - dens to bear, No more

clouds in the sky, no more tears to dim the eye; All is peace
sick - ness, no pain, no more part - ing o - ver there; And for - ev -

for - ev - er - more on that hap - py gold - en shore, What a day glo - ri - ous
er   I will be with the One who died for me,

CHORUS

day that will be.   What a day that will be when my Je - sus

I shall see, And I look up - on His face, the One who saved me

What A Day That Will Be

by His grace; When He takes me by the hand, and leads me through the

Prom-ised Land, What a day, glo - ri - ous day that will be.

25 How Beautiful Heaven Must Be

MRS. A. S. BRIDGEWATER.   A. P. BLAND.

1. We read of a place that's called heaven, It's made for the pure and the free;
2. In heav-en no drooping nor pin-ing, No wish-ing for else-where to be;
3. Pure wa-ters of life there are flow-ing, And all who will drink may be free;
4. The an - gels so sweet-ly are sing-ing, Up there by the beau-ti - ful sea;

FINE

These truths in God's word He hath giv - en, How beau-ti - ful heav-en must be.
God's light is for - ev - er there shin-ing, How beau-ti - ful heav-en must be.
Rare jew - els of splendor are glow-ing, How beau-ti - ful heav-en must be.
Sweet chords from their gold harps are ring-ing, How beau-ti - ful heav-en must be.

D. S. Fair ha-ven of rest for the wear - y, How beau-ti - ful heav-en must be.

REFRAIN.   D. S.

How beau-ti - ful heav-en must be, must be, Sweet home of the hap - py and free;

26
Come And Dine

Words and melody by C. C. Widmeyer

S. H. Bolton

1. Je - sus has a ta - ble spread Where the saints of God are fed,
2. The dis - ci - ples came to land, Thus o - bey - ing Christ's command,
3. Soon the Lamb will take His bride To be ev - er at His side,

He in - vites His chos - en peo - ple "Come and dine;" With His man - na
For the Mas - ter called un - to them "Come and dine;" There they found their
All the host of heav-en will as - sem-bled be; O, 'twill be a

He doth feed And sup-plies our ev - 'ry need; O 'tis sweet to sup with
hearts' de - sire, Bread and fish up - on the fire; Thus He sat - is - fies the
glo - rious sight, All the saints in spot-less white; And with Je - sus they will

CHORUS

Je - sus all the time!
hun - gry ev - 'ry time. "Come and, dine," the Mas - ter call - eth, "Come and
feast e - ter - nal - ly.

dine;" You may feast at Je - sus' ta - ble all the
O come and dine;

Come And Dine

time; ... He who fed the mul-ti-tude, Turned the

O come and dine;

wa-ter in-to wine, To the hun-gry call-eth now, "Come and dine."

27   Leaning On The Everlasting Arms

Rev. E. A. Hoffman   A. J. Showalter

1. What a fel-low-ship, what a joy di-vine, Leaning on the ev-er-last-ing arms;
2. O how sweet to walk in the pilgrim way, Leaning on the ev-er-last-ing arms;
3. What have I to dread, what have I to fear, Leaning on the ev-er-last-ing arms;

What a bless-ed-ness, what a peace is mine, Leaning on the ev-er-lasting arms.
O how bright the path grows from day to day, Leaning on the ev-er-lasting arms.
I have bless-ed peace with my Lord so near, Leaning on the ev-er-lasting arms.

CHORUS

Lean - ing lean - ing Safe and secure from all alarms; Leaning on the everlasting arms.
Leaning on Jesus, leaning on Jesus,

Take The Name Of Jesus With You

Mrs. Lydia Baxter.

W. H. Doane.

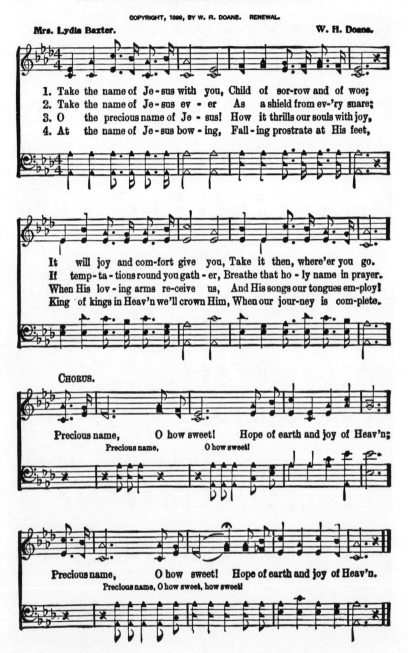

1. Take the name of Je-sus with you, Child of sor-row and of woe;
2. Take the name of Je-sus ev - er As a shield from ev-'ry snare;
3. O the precious name of Je - sus! How it thrills our souls with joy,
4. At the name of Je-sus bow-ing, Fall-ing prostrate at His feet,

It will joy and com-fort give you, Take it then, where'er you go.
If temp-ta-tions round you gath-er, Breathe that ho-ly name in prayer.
When His lov-ing arms re-ceive us, And His songs our tongues em-ploy!
King of kings in Heav'n we'll crown Him, When our jour-ney is com-plete.

CHORUS.

Precious name, O how sweet! Hope of earth and joy of Heav'n;
Precious name, O how sweet!

Precious name, O how sweet! Hope of earth and joy of Heav'n.
Precious name, O how sweet, how sweet!

Crown Of Thorns

J. D.   Jimmie Davis
J. M.   Jack Mainord

1. There have been kings with riches untold, They have worn crowns of diamonds and gold.
2. They were so cruel to Je- sus our king He died for sins, Sal- va-tion to bring.

But there's a king who was battered and torn and the crown that He wore was a crown
He's king of kings, The great-est e'er born

(Hmm)

CHORUS

of thorns. A crown of thorns was placed on His head, He hung on the

(Hmm)

cross un - til He was dead. The sky was dark with a rag-ing storm

(Hmm)

when they crowned the king of kings with a crown of thorns.

It's Different Now

Arrangement by David Beatty

1. Once I was lost in sin, I had no peace with-in, To save my
2. I went to church one day to hear them sing and pray, The preach-er
3. Sin's fet-ters held me fast, the dye was al-most cast, My proud and
4. And now my hopes are bright, I praise Him day and night, How He could

wea-ry soul I knew not how; But Je-sus came to me, and
firm-ly plowed the gos-pel plow; He said you must re-pent, so
haugh-ty spir-it would not bow; But just one glimpse of Him, it
change me so I know not how; But praise the Lord it's done, the

by His grace I'm free,
down the aisle I went, Now it's dif-f'rent so dif-f'rent
broke the pow'r of sin, yes, it's
vic-t'ry now is won,

CHORUS

now. It's dif-f'rent now, Since Je-sus saved my
Yes, it's dif-f'rent now,

soul, It's dif-f'rent now, since by His blood I'm
since He saved my soul, Yes, it's dif-frent now,

When We All Get To Heaven

E. E. Hewitt.   Mrs. J. G. Wilson.

1. Sing the won-drous love of Je-sus, Sing His mer-cy and His grace;
2. While we walk the pil-grim path-way, Clouds will o-ver-spread the sky;
3. Let us then be true and faith-ful, Trust-ing, serv-ing ev-'ry day;
4. On-ward to the prize be-fore us! Soon His beau-ty we'll be-hold;

In the man-sions, bright and blessed, He'll pre-pare for us a place.
But when trav-'ling days are o-ver, Not a shad-ow, not a sigh.
Just one glimpse of Him in glo-ry Will the toils of life re-pay.
Soon the pearl-y gates will o-pen, We shall tread the streets of gold.
for us a place.

Chorus.

When we all get to heav-en, What a day of re-
When we all   What a

joic-ing that will be! When we all see
day of re-joic-ing that will be! When we all

Je-sus, We'll sing and shout the vic-to-ry.
shout, and shout the vic-to-ry.

It's Different Now

whole;
by His blood I'm whole;

Old Sa-tan had to flee when Je-sus res-cued me,
Ah............ ah............

Now it's dif-f'rent,
yes, it's

O   so dif-f'rent now.
so dif-f'rent now.

O How I Love Jesus

3 1

1. There is a name I love to hear, I love to sing its worth; It sounds like
2. It   tells me of a Sav-ior's love, Who died to set me free;   It tells me
3. It   tells me what my Fa-ther hath In store for ev-'ry day, And tho I
4. It   tells of One whose loving heart Can feel my deepest woe, Who in each

CHORUS

mu - sic in mine ear, The sweetest name on earth.
of His pre-cious blood, The sinner's perfect plea. Oh, how I love Je-sus,
tread a darksome path, Yields sunshine all the way..
sor - row bears a part, That none can bear below.

Oh, how I love Je-sus,   Oh, how I love Je-sus, Be-cause He first loved me!

Are You Washed In The Blood?

E. A. Hoffman

1. Have you been to Je - sus for the cleansing pow'r? Are you washed in the
2. Are you walk-ing dai - ly by the Sav-ior's side? Are you washed in the
3. When the Bridegroom cometh will your robes be white, Pure and white in the
4. Lay a - side the garments that are stained with sin, And be washed in the

blood of the Lamb? Are you ful - ly trust - ing in His grace this hour?
blood of the Lamb? Do you rest each mo-ment in the Cru - ci - fied?
blood of the Lamb? Will your soul be read - y for the mansions bright?
blood of the Lamb; There's a foun - tain flow-ing for the soul un-clean,

CHORUS

Are you washed in the blood of the Lamb? Are you washed in the
Are you washed in the blood of the Lamb?
And be washed in the blood of the Lamb?
O be washed in the blood of the Lamb! Are you washed

blood, In the soul-cleansing blood of the Lamb? Are your
in the blood, of the Lamb?

garments spot - less, are they white as snow? Are you washed in the blood of the Lamb?

Follow Me

I. F. S.   Ira F. Stanphill

1. I trav-eled down a lone-ly road And no one seemed to care, The bur-den
2. "I work so hard for Je - sus" I of - ten boast and say, "I've sac-ri-
3. Oh, Je - sus if I die up-on A for-eign field some day, 'T would be no

on my wea-ry back Had bowed me to de-spair, I oft complained to Je-
ficed a lot of things To walk the nar-row way, I gave up fame and for-
more than love demands No less could I re-pay, "No great-er love hath mortal

sus How folks were treating me, And then I heard Him say so ten-der-ly,
tune; I'm worth a lot to Thee," And then I hear Him gen-tly say to me,
man Than for a friend to die" These are the words He gen-tly spoke to me,

"My feet were al - so wea-ry, Up-on the Cal-v'ry road; The cross be-
"I left the throne of glo-ry And counted it but loss, My hands were
"If just a cup of wa-ter I place with-in your hand Then just a

came so heav-y, I fell be-neath the load, Be faith-ful wea-ry pil-grim
nailed in an-ger Up-on a cru-el cross, But now we'll make the jour-ney
cup of wa-ter Is all that I de-mand, But if by death to liv-ing

Follow Me

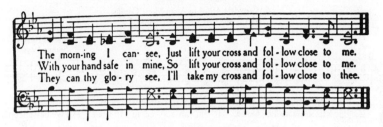

The morn-ing I can see, Just lift your cross and fol-low close to me.
With your hand safe in mine, So lift your cross and fol-low close to me.
They can thy glo-ry see, I'll take my cross and fol-low close to thee.

35 Precious Memories

Words and Melody J. B. F. WRIGHT   ARR. for JOHN T. BENSON, JR.

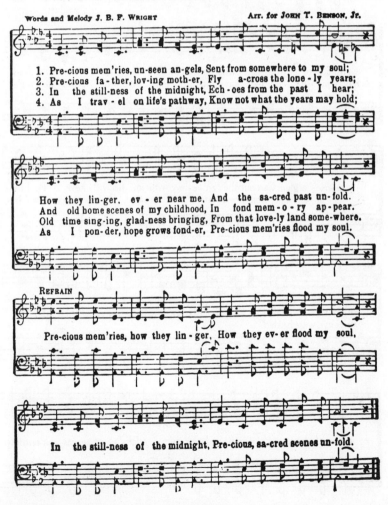

1. Pre-cious mem'ries, un-seen an-gels, Sent from somewhere to my soul;
2. Pre-cious fa-ther, lov-ing moth-er, Fly a-cross the lone-ly years;
3. In the still-ness of the midnight, Ech-oes from the past I hear;
4. As I trav-el on life's pathway, Know not what the years may hold;

How they lin-ger, ev-er near me, And the sa-cred past un-fold.
And old home scenes of my childhood, In fond mem-o-ry ap-pear.
Old time sing-ing, glad-ness bringing, From that love-ly land some-where.
As I pon-der, hope grows fond-er, Pre-cious mem'ries flood my soul.

REFRAIN

Pre-cious mem'ries, how they lin-ger, How they ev-er flood my soul,

In the still-ness of the midnight, Pre-cious, sa-cred scenes un-fold.

By His Stripes Ye Were Healed

E. H.
J. D.

Everett Hurley
Jimmie Davis

1. He bore stripes on His back to touch the lame and make them walk; The blinded eyes
2. "By His stripes we'll be healed," Is - ai - ah stat - ed in His book; "All we like sheep

were made to see the man who came from Gal - i - lee. He made the dead
have gone astray, and we have turned to our own way." A - pos - tle Pe-

to rise a-gain, Cast out the en - e - my with-in; Just be - lieve, By His
ter la - ter came, Confirmed that it was still the same, "By His stripes By His

CHORUS

stripes ye were healed. By His stripes ye were healed, says the Bible; By His
stripes ye were healed."

stripes He bore your sor - row and your pain. Ev - 'ry stripe was writ-ten down,

By His Stripes Ye Were Healed

For I know a need was found. By His stripes, By His stripes ye were healed

We Shall Shine As The Stars

37

J. W. V.

J. W. Van Deventer
Arr. Amanda Jarrett

1. We may tar - ry a while here as strangers, Unnoticed by those who pass by;
2. We may nev-er be rich in earth's treasures, Nor rise on the lad-der of fame;
3. We may live in a tent or a cot-tage, And die in se-clu-sion unknown;

But the Sav-iour will crown us in glo-ry, To shine as the stars of the sky.
But the saints will at last be reward-ed, Made rich in Imman-u-el's name.
But the Fa-ther who see-eth in se-cret, Re-members each one of His own.

CHORUS

We shall shine as the stars of the morning, With Je-sus the cru-ci-fied one;

We shall rise to be like Him for-ev-er, E-ter-nal-ly shine as the sun.

Robe of Calvary

Words and Music by Kathleen Twomey, ASCAP
Fred White, ASCAP,
Robert St. Clair and Elaine Rivers

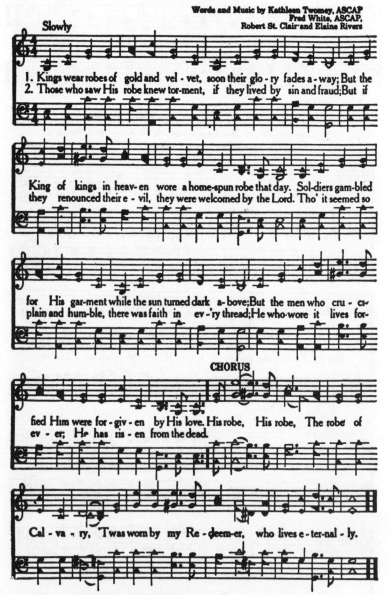

1. Kings wear robes of gold and vel - vet, soon their glo - ry fades a - way; But the
2. Those who saw His robe knew tor-ment, if they lived by sin and fraud; But if

King of kings in heav - en wore a home-spun robe that day. Sol-diers gam-bled
they renounced their e - vil, they were welcomed by the Lord. Tho' it seemed so

for His gar-ment while the sun turned dark a-bove; But the men who cru - ci-
plain and hum-ble, there was faith in ev - 'ry thread; He who wore it lives for-

CHORUS

fied Him were for - giv - en by His love. His robe, His robe, The robe of
ev - er; He has ris - en from the dead.

Cal - va - ry, 'Twas worn by my Re - deem-er, who lives e - ter-nal - ly.

Jesus Brings Sweet Joy To Me

As sung by The Sisk Family

T. S.

Theodore Sisk

1. When I feel so lone-some, sad and blue, Je-sus brings sweet joy to
2. When the storm-y bil-lows round me roll,
3. When I reach the gates of glo-ry land,

me; Giv-ing me a song the whole day thru, Je-sus brings sweet
To His lov-ing hand I'll firm-ly hold,
Joy to me; I shall then be one of that glad band,

joy to me.

Chorus

Je-sus brings sweet joy to me,
Joy to me. brings won-der-ful joy to me,

What a hap-py mel-o-dy; Sing-ing out the sto-ry,
hap-py mel-o-dy;

give to God the glo-ry, Je-sus brings sweet joy to me, joy to me.

Jesus Holds The Keys

Words by V. B. E. and
W. F. (Bill) Lakey
©Copyright, 1956, by V. B. (Vep) Ellis
Music by
V. B. (Vep) Ellis

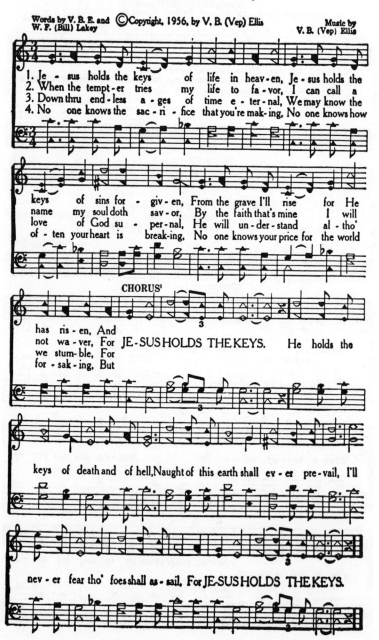

41 The Blood That Stained The Old Rugged Cross

A. E. B.

Albert E. Brumley

Count Your Blessings

Rev. Johnson Oatman, Jr.

E. O. Excell

1. When up-on life's bil-lows you are tem - pest - tossed, When you are dis-
2. Are you ev - er burdened with a load of care? Does the cross seem
3. When you look at oth-ers with their lands and gold, Think that Christ has
4. So, a-mid the con-flict, whether great or small, Do not be dis-

cour-aged, thinking all is lost, Count your man-y blessings, name them
heav-y you are called to bear? Count your man-y blessings, ev-'ry
prom-ised you His wealth un - told; Count your man-y blessings, mon-ey
cour-aged, God is o - - ver all; Count your man-y blessings, an-gels

one by one, And it will sur-prise you what the Lord hath done.
doubt will fly, And you will be sing-ing as the days go by.
can - - not buy Your re-ward in heav-en, nor your home on high.
will at - - tend, Help and comfort give you to your jour - ney's end.

CHORUS

Count your blessings, Name them one by one; Count your
Count your man-y blessings, Name them one by one; Count your man - y

bless-ings, See what God hath done; Count your bless-ings,
bless-ings, See what God hath done; Count your man-y bless-ings,

Count Your Blessings

Rit. a tempo

Name them one by one; Count your man-y bless-ings, See what God hath done.

43 Heaven Will Surely Be Worth It All

Copyright, 1946, by O. A. Parris in "Charming Refuge"

W. Oliver Cooper   Assigned 1947, to Stamps Quartet Music Co., Inc.   Minzo C. Jones

1. Of - ten I'm hin-dered on my way, Burdened so heav-y I al-most fall;
2. Man-y the tri - als, toils and tears, Man - y a heart-ache may here ap- pall;
3. Toil-ing and pain I will en - dure, Till I shall hear the death an- gel call;

Then I hear Je - sus sweet-ly say;
But the dear Lord so true - ly says; "Heaven will sure - ly be worth it all."
Je - sus has promised and I'm sure

CHORUS

Heav - en will sure - ly be worth it all, Worth all the sor-rows that here be - fall;

Aft - er this life with all its strife; Heav-en will sure - ly be worth it all.

Just A Closer Walk With Thee

Anon.

Arr. for John T. Benson

1. I am weak but Thou art strong (Thou art strong), Je-sus keep me from all
2. Thru this world of toil and snares (toil and snares), If I fal-ter, Lord, who
3. When my fee-ble life is o'er (life is o'er), Time for me will be no

wrong (from all wrong); I'll be sat-is-fied as long (just as long), As I walk let me
cares (Lord, who cares)? Who with me my burden shares (burden shares)? None but Thee, dear
more (be no more); Guide me gently, safely o'er (safely o'er), To Thy king-dom

CHORUS.

walk close to Thee (close to Thee).
Lord, none but Thee (none but Thee). Just a closer walk with Thee (walk with Thee),
shore, to Thy shore (to Thy shore).

Grant it, Je-sus, is my plea (hum-ble plea); Dai-ly walk-ing close to

Thee (close to Thee), Let it be, dear Lord, let it be (let it be).

Hide Me, Rock Of Ages

Brantley C. George

1. O   thou blessed Rock of A - ges, (Rock of A - ges, I am) Trust-ing
2. Keep me when the storm-clouds gather, (storm-clouds gath-er, keep me) Till the
3. When my journey is com-plet - ed, (is com-plet - ed, Sav-ior) And there's

now dear Lord in Thee; (dear Lord in Thee I'm trusting) Keep me till my
sun comes shin-ing thrn; (comes shining thru the shadows) Keep me till my
no more work to do; (no work to do, O bless-ed) Sav - ior guide my

D. S.-When the storm a-
FINE

jour-ney's end-ed, (journey's ended, Keep me) Till Thy blessed face I   see.
work is o - ver, (work is o - ver, Keep me) Till I bid this world a - dieu.
wea - ry spir-it, (wea - ry spir - it, To that) Hap-py land be-yond the blue.

round me rag-es, (round me rag - es, Bless-ed) Rock of A - ges hide Thou me.

REFRAIN

Hide me, O blest Rock of A - - - ges,
A - ges, Rock of A - ges, hide me,

D. S.

Till Thy bless - ed face I   see; (Thy face I   see, in glo - ry)

46 Neither Do I Condemn Thee

Arr. C. S. & J. S.

Arr. by Carol Snow & Jimmy Snow

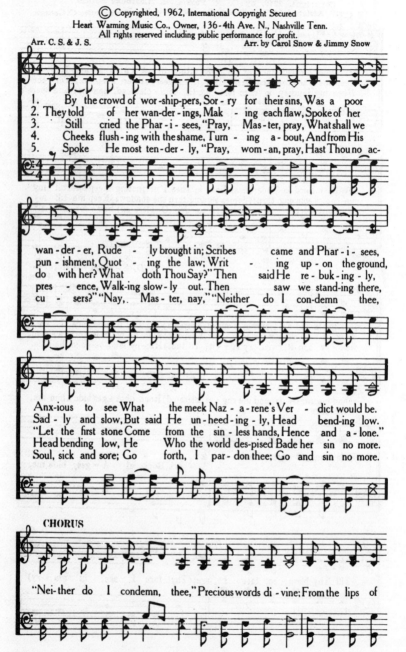

1. By the crowd of wor-ship-pers, Sor-ry for their sins, Was a poor
2. They told of her wan-der-ings, Mak-ing each flaw, Spoke of her
3. Still cried the Phar-i-sees, "Pray, Mas-ter, pray, What shall we
4. Cheeks flush-ing with the shame, Turn-ing a-bout, And from His
5. Spoke He most ten-der-ly, "Pray, wom-an, pray, Hast Thou no ac-

wan-der-er, Rude-ly brought in; Scribes came and Phar-i-sees,
pun-ishment, Quot-ing the law; Writ-ing up-on the ground,
do with her? What doth Thou Say?" Then said He re-buk-ing-ly,
pres-ence, Walk-ing slow-ly out. Then saw we stand-ing there,
cu-sers?" "Nay, Mas-ter, nay," "Neither do I con-demn thee,

Anx-ious to see What the meek Naz-a-rene's Ver-dict would be.
Sad-ly and slow, But said He un-heed-ing-ly, Head bend-ing low.
"Let the first stone Come from the sin-less hands, Hence and a-lone."
Head bending low, He Who the world des-pised Bade her sin no more.
Soul, sick and sore; Go forth, I par-don thee; Go and sin no more.

CHORUS

"Nei-ther do I condemn, thee," Precious words di-vine; From the lips of

Neither Do I Condemn Thee

mer - cy Like the sweet-est chimes. Wonder-ful words of Je - sus,

Sing them o'er and o'er; "Neither do I con-demn thee, Go and sin no more."

47

Jesus, Savior, Pilot Me

Edward Hopper   J. E. Gould

1. Je - sus, Sav - ior, pi - lot me O - ver life's tem - pes-tuous sea:
2. As a moth - er stills her child, Thou canst hush the o - cean wild;
3. When at last I near the shore, And the fear - ful break-ers roar

Un-known waves be - fore me roll, Hid - ing rocks and treacherous shoal;
Bois-terous waves o - bey Thy will When Thou sayest to them, "Be still!"
'Twixt me and the peace-ful rest, Then, while lean - ing on Thy breast,

Chart and com - pass come from Thee, Je - sus, Sav - ior, pi - lot me.
Won-drous Sov-ereign of the sea, Je - sus, Sav - ior, pi - lot me.
May I hear Thee say to me, "Fear not, I. will pi - lot thee."

My Room Of Prayer

J. C.

Jan Crutchfield

There's a room that I can go to And I feel the Master's lov-ing
Oo Oo

hand As I kneel down and pray, I feel Him so close to me.
Oo Ah so close to me.

No mat-ter when I call up-on Him I can al-ways find Him wait-ing
Ah Oo

there. There's a room where I go, I call it my room of prayer.

CHORUS

My room of prayer, My room of prayer.
my room of prayer my room of prayer.

My Room Of Prayer

The Lord and I can be to-geth-er right there.
the Lord and I can be to-geth-er right there.

When I am down I nev-er wor-ry for if I have more than I can
Ah Oo

bear, I just go to the room, I call it my room of prayer.

Footsteps Of Jesus

49 Mrs. M. B. Slade   Dr. A. B. Everett

1. Sweetly, Lord, have we heard Thee calling, Come follow me! And we see where Thy
2. Tho they lead o'er the cold dark mountains, Seeking His sheep; Or a-long by Si-
3. If they lead thru the tem-ple ho-ly, Preaching the Word; Or in homes of the
4. By and by thru the shining portals, Turn-ing our feet, We shall walk with the
5. Then at last when on high He sees us, Our jour-ney done, We shall rest where the

Fine Chorus   D.S.—We will fol-low the

foot-prints falling, Lead us to Thee.
foam's fountains, Helping the weak.
poor and low-ly, Serving the Lord. Footprints of Jesus, That makes the pathway glow,
glad immortals, Heav'n's golden street.
steps of Jesus End at His throne.

D. S.

steps of Jesus, Where'er they go.

Lovest Thou Me?

50

Second Verse
David Ingles

Words and Music
Steve Pringle

1. Lov-est thou Me more than these, O Lord you know I do;
2. Lov-est thou Me more than these, He's ask-ing you and me;

Then feed My sheep they are hun-gry and cold; Shel-ter my lambs
Then feed His sheep they need manna from a-bove; Refuge in the arms

CHORUS

in the fold (in the fold) There are nine-ty and nine safe in the
of His love (of His love)

fold, But one has gone a-stray; So I'll search on the moun-tain

dark and cold, And bring back the lost one to the fold-(to the fold)

Far Above The Starry Sky

T. S.   Theodore Sisk

1. Soon I'll leave this world of sor-row,   For that homeland of the soul;
2. Soon I'll walk the streets of glo - ry,   Meet with loved ones gone be-fore,
3. Come and go with me to glo-ry,   From all sor-row we'll be free,

It will be a bright to-mor-row, When the pearl-y gates un-fold; Sav-ior,
O what shouting, O what sing-ing, When He o-pens wide the door; Christ Him
Then we'll sing love's grand old sto - ry, Just a-cross the jas-per sea; With my

be thou ev - er near me, Till I reach my home on high, Where I'll rest from
self will come to greet me, To that hap-py home on high, He will give to
harp and crown I'll ev - er Play the song, "sweet by and by," With the hosts of

FINE CHORUS

all my la - bor,
me a wel-come, Far a-bove the star-ry sky. 'Twill be glo - ry, hal-le-
heav-en join - ing,

D. S.

lu-jah, No, I'll nev-er know a sigh, In the hap-py new Je - ru - sa-lem,

Ten Thousand Angels

R O.

Ray Overholt

mp Slowly, with much feeling

1. They bound the hands of Je-sus in the gar-den where He prayed; They
2. Up - - on His pre-cious head they placed a crown of thorns; They
3. When they nailed Him to the Cross, His moth-er stood near-by; He
4. To the howl-ing mob He yield-ed; He did not for mer-cy cry. The

led Him thro the streets in shame. They spat up-on the Sav-iour so
laughed and said,"Be-hold the King." They struck Him and they cursed Him and
said, "Wom-an, be-hold thy son!" He cried, "I thirst for wa-ter," but they
Cross of shame He took a-lone. And when He cried,"It's fin-ished,"He

pure and free from sin; They said, "Cru-ci-fy Him; He's to blame."
mocked His ho-ly name. All a-lone He suf-fered ev-'ry-thing.
gave Him none to drink. Then the sin-ful work of man was done.
gave him-self to die; Sal - - va-tion's won-drous plan was done.

CHORUS
f Faster

He could have called ten thou-sand an-gels To de-stroy the

world and set Him free. He could have called,
the world

Ten Thousand Angels

ten thou-sand an-gels, But He died a-lone, for you and me.

a-lone

53

Beautiful Isle

Jessie B. Pounds

J. S. Fearis
Arranged by John T. Benson, Jr.

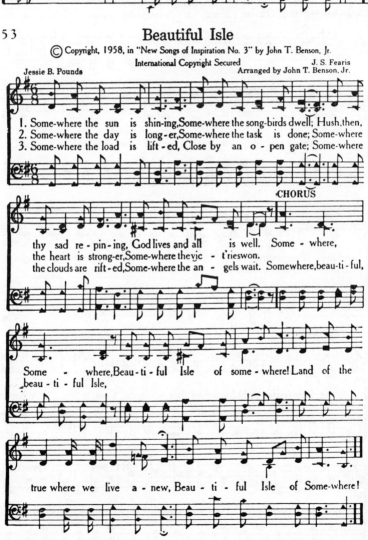

1. Some-where the sun is shin-ing, Some-where the song-birds dwell; Hush, then,
2. Some-where the day is long-er, Some-where the task is done; Some-where
3. Some-where the load is lift-ed, Close by an o-pen gate; Some-where

CHORUS

thy sad re-pin-ing, God lives and all is well. Some-where,
the heart is strong-er, Some-where the vic-t'ries won.
the clouds are rift-ed, Some-where the an-gels wait. Somewhere, beau-ti-ful,

Some - where, Beau-ti-ful Isle of some-where! Land of the
beau-ti-ful Isle,

true where we live a-new, Beau-ti-ful Isle of Some-where!

54

When I Prayed Last Night

J. D.

Jimmie Davis

1. Oh, my heart was so trou-bled that I knelt down to pray, It was then
2. Yes, my dear moth-er told me, a long time a-go, "Trust in Je-sus

that I first saw the light; Je-sus put His arms a-round me I
He will make your fu-ture bright" Now I un-der-stand the mean-ing

saw the scars in His hand. I saw Je-sus when I prayed last night.
of His wonder-ful love.

CHORUS

When I prayed last night I heard my Sav-ior say "Come to Me, I will make

your bur-dens light;" Then we walked through the val-ley And we

When I Prayed Last Night

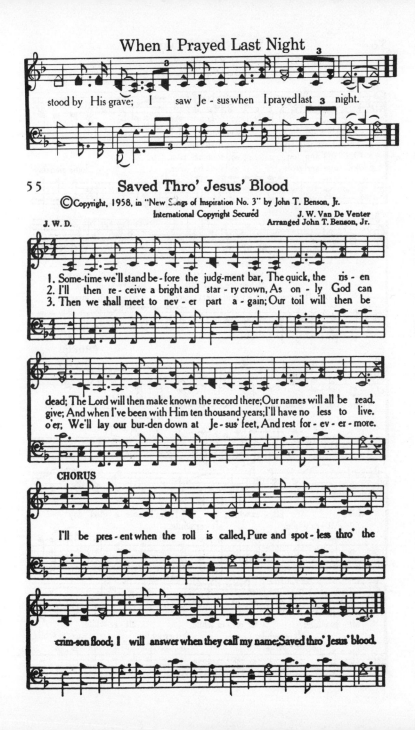

stood by His grave; I saw Je - sus when I prayed last night.

55 Saved Thro' Jesus' Blood

© Copyright, 1958, in "New Songs of Inspiration No. 3" by John T. Benson, Jr.
International Copyright Secured

J. W. Van De Venter
Arranged John T. Benson, Jr.

J. W. D.

1. Some-time we'll stand be - fore the judg-ment bar, The quick, the ris - en
2. I'll then re - ceive a bright and star - ry crown, As on - ly God can
3. Then we shall meet to nev - er part a - gain; Our toil will then be

dead; The Lord will then make known the record there; Our names will all be read.
give; And when I've been with Him ten thousand years; I'll have no less to live.
o'er; We'll lay our bur-den down at Je - sus' feet, And rest for - ev - er - more.

CHORUS

I'll be pres - ent when the roll is called, Pure and spot - less thro' the

crim-son flood; I will answer when they call my name; Saved thro' Jesus' blood.

Some Glad Day

56

W. M. R.

Will M. Ramsey
Arranged John T. Benson, Jr.

1. O bless-ed tho't....... sweet rest will come,..... Some glad day
2. These heav-y loads........ we shall lay down,.....
3. Our suff'ring too....... will soon be past,......
4. All war and strife....... will soon be o'er....... Some glad day

aft - er while; When all our toil........ on earth is done,......
When we re-ceive....... our heav'nly crown,.....
When we shall find...... sweet rest at last,.......
aft - er while; We'll find sweet peace...... on heaven's shore.......

CHORUS

There'll come a glad day   aft - er while.   O aft - er
aft - er while.

while,   aft - er while,   There'll come a glad day
Aft - er while,   aft - er while,

aft - er while;   O aft - er while,   aft - er while,
aft - er while;   Aft-er while,   aft - er while.

Some Glad Day

There'll come a glad day aft - er while.

aft - er while.

57   Farther Along

B. E. Warren   Copyright, MCMXLIV, in Radiant Joy,   R. E. Winsett
Original words owned by R. E. W.   by R. E. Winsett, Dayton, Tenn.

1. Tempted and tried we're oft made to wander Why it should be thus all the day long;
2. Sometimes I wonder why I must suf-fer, Go in the cold, the rain and the snow;
3. Tempted and tried how of-ten we question Why we must suf-fer year af-ter year;
4. Of - ten when death has tak-en our loved ones, Leav-ing our home so lone and so drear;
5. "Faithful till death," saith our loving Mas-ter; Short is our time to la-bor and wait;
6. Soon we will see our dear loving Sav-ior, Hear the last trumpet sound thro' the sky;

FINE

While there are oth-ers liv-ing a-bout us, Nev-er mo-lest-ed, tho' in the wrong.
While many wick-ed live in great splendor, Heedless of where at last they must go.
Be - ing accused by those of our loved ones, E'en tho' we walk in God's ho-ly fear.
Then do we wonder why others prosper, Liv-ing so wick-ed year af-ter year.
Then will our toiling seem to be noth-ing, When we shall pass the heav-en-ly gate.
Then we will meet those gone on be-fore us, And we shall know and understand why.

D.S. Cheer up my brother, live in the sunshine, We'll understand it all by and by.

REFRAIN   **D. S.**

Farther a-long we'll know all a-bout it, Farther a-long we'll un-der-stand why;

I Want to See Jesus First of All

J.D. Jimmie Davis

1. Tho' I may be a pau-per and may dress in rags, While trav-'ling this
2. When my loved ones for-sake me and friends turn a-way, When I need some-
3. When my ship comes to an-chor on Jordan's great banks, And I step on

rock-y old road, But to see my Sav-iour will be well worth it all,
bod-y to care, Then I turn to my Sav-iour and He smiles and says,
that gold-en shore, I'll shake hands with all of the Saints gone on be-fore,

CHORUS

When we meet in that cit-y of gold.
"I am with thee child nev-er fear." When I put on my robe of
But I want to see Je-sus first of all.

spark-ling white, and a crown of diamonds and gold. I'll meet all my loved

ones and friends I have known, But I want to see Je-sus first of all.

My Heart's Desire

1. My heart longs not, for world-ly pleasures, So man-y here ad-mire;
2. To lend a hand to a fall-en broth-er, To lift some soul from the mire;
3. Let me not work when all is well, No fame nor wealth ac-quire;

To count my wealth by Heav-en's mea - sures,
To show Christ's love one to an - oth - er, Is my heart's de - sire.
To open a mission next door to hell,

CHORUS

My de - sire, my de - sire, That's my heart's de - sire; To
count my wealth by Heav-en's mea - sures, Is my heart's de - sire.

FIVE MINUTES AFTER I DIE
J. B. Thomas
Jimmie Davis

Life is like a weaver's shuttle, Swiftly passing by;
Earthly things will hold no value, Five minutes after I die.
All the good that I intended, For some weary passerby;
Will scorch my soul like burning embers, Five minutes after I die.

To me my money will be worthless, It has no value in the sky;
I'd give the world for God's sweet presence, Five minutes after I die.
Let me haste while serving others, List mine ear for a needy cry;
That I may feel I've done my portion, Five minutes after I die.

Christ Is The Answer

J. D.
W. F.

Jimmie Davis
Wally Fowler

1. Soul are you wea - ry, does life seem drear-y? "What shall I do?" I
2. Je - sus is plead-ing, friends, are you heeding? He'll hear you call, He'll
3. Sin and temp - ta - tion now fill our na - tion, Sometime it seems that

heard someone say; Come, hear my story, I've found the glory,
save you to-day; Burdens He'll lighten, Dark clouds He'll brighten, Christ is the answer
all hope is gone; Turn, then to Je-sus, From sin He'll free us,

CHORUS

He'll save your soul to - day.
Just hum-bly kneel and pray. Christ is the an-swer, He is the Sav - ior,
Till glo - ry morn shall dawn.

He is the rul - er of this world, He'll nev - er leave us,

And ne'er de-ceive us, March on, oh, Christians, and keep His flag un-furled.

You Can Have Him

61

J. D.
J. M.

Jack Mainord
Jimmie Davis

1. Once my life was filled with problems, I did - n't have no place to go;
Christ is might - y emp - ty, al - tho' you have all the wealth untold;

Oo   Oo

And then I found a friend in Jesus, There was contentment for my soul.
Get on your knees now and pray to Je-sus, He'll guide your feet to that shining goal.

Ah   Oo

Well, you can have Him If you want Him He will protect
You can have Him, If you want Him

you ev - 'ry day He on - ly wants you to love and trust Him,
He'll pro-tect you ev - 'ry day,

Ah

He'll save your soul and come in to stay 2. Life without stay
save your soul come in to stay. come in to stay.

Invisible Hands

Words and Music by Buddy Kaye, Bill Harrington,
Frank Stanton and Fred Patrick

1. In - vis - i - ble hands.......... are wait - ing to guide you,
2. In - vis - i - ble hands.......... will keep you from dan - ger,

In - vis - i - ble hands........ will show you the way, will show you the way;
In - vis - i - ble hands....... will keep you from harm, will keep you from harm;

Have faith in the Lord,........ He's al - ways be - side you,
Tho' you may have sinned,........ God wel - comes a stran - ger,

So pray and be - lieve, and help you'll re - ceive from in - vis - i - ble hands.

FINE

CHORUS

In - vis - i - ble hands,
Are wait - ing to guide you, in - vis - i - ble

Invisible Hands

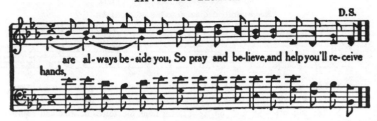

are al-ways be-side you, So pray and be-lieve, and help you'll re-ceive hands,

Blessed Assurance

Fanny J. Crosby

Mrs. Joseph F. Knapp

1. Bless-ed as-sur-ance, Je-sus is mine! O what a for-taste of
2. Per-fect sub-mis-sion, per-fect de-light, Vi-sions of rap-ture now
3. Per-fect sub-mis-sion, all is at rest, I in my Sav-iour am

glo-ry di-vine! Heir of sal-va-tion, pur-chase of God,
burst on my sight. An-gels de-scend-ing bring from a-bove,
hap-py and blest. Watching and wait-ing, look-ing a-bove,

FINE   CHORUS

Born of His Spir-it, washed in His blood.
Ech-oes of mer-cy, whis-pers of love. This is my sto-ry, this is my song,
Filled with His goodness, lost in His love.

D. S.-Prais-ing my Sav-iour all the day long.

D. S.

Prais-ing my Sav-iour all the day long; This is my sto-ry, this is my song,

Life's Railway To Heaven

Respectfully dedicated to the railroad men.

M. E. ABBEY.

CHARLIE D. TILLMAN.

SOLO or DUET. Tempo ad lib.

1. Life is like a mountain rail - road, With an en - gi-neer that's brave;
2. You will roll up grades of tri - al; You will cross the bridge of strife;
3. You will oft - en find ob-struc-tions; Look for storms of wind and rain;
4. As you roll a - cross the tres - tle, Spanning Jor - dan's swell-ing tide,

We must make the run suc - cess-ful, From the cra - dle to the grave;
See that Christ is your con - duc - tor On this light-ning train of life;
On a fill, or curve, or tres-tle, They will al-most ditch your train;
You be - hold the Un - ion De - pot In - to which your train will glide;

Watch the curves, the fills, the tun - nels; Nev - er fal - ter, nev - er quail;
Al - ways mind - ful of ob - struc-tion, Do your du - ty, nev - er fail;
Put your trust a - lone in Je - sus; Nev - er fal - ter, nev - er fail;
There you'll meet the Su - perin-ten-dent, God, the Fa - ther, God, the Son,

Rit.

Keep your hand up - on the throt-tle, And your eye up - on the rail.
Keep your hand up - on the throt-tle, And your eye up - on the rail.
Keep your hand up - on the throt-tle, And your eye up - on the rail.
With the heart - y, joy - ous plaud-it, " Wea - ry pil - grim, welcome home."

Life's Railway To Heaven

Bless-ed Sav-ior, Thou wilt guide us, Till we reach that bliss-ful shore,

Where the an-gels wait to join us In Thy praise for-ev-er-more.

65

Cleanse Me

J. Edwin Orr

Maori Melody
Arranged John T. Benson, Jr.

1. Search me, O God, and know my heart to-day; Try me, O
2. I praise Thee, Lord, for cleans-ing me from sin; Ful-fill Thy
3. Lord, take my life, and make it whol-ly Thine; Fill my poor
4. O Ho-ly Ghost, re-viv-al comes from Thee; Send a re-

Sav-ior, know my tho'ts, I pray: See if there be some wick-ed
Word, and make me pure with-in; Fill me with fire, where once I
heart with Thy great love di-vine; Take all my will, my pas-sion,
viv-al, start the work in me: Thy Word de-clares Thou wilt sup-

way in me: Cleanse me from ev-'ry sin, and set me free.
burned with shame: Grant my de-sire to mag-ni-fy Thy name.
self and pride; I now sur-ren-der: Lord, in me a-bide.
ply our need: For bless-ing now, O Lord, I hum-bly plead.

66 I Wouldn't Take Nothin' For My Journey

Copyright 1964 by Jimmie Davis Music Co., Inc., 836 Rutherford St., Shreveport, La.
International copyright secured. Printed in U. S. A.

C. G.
J. D.

Charles Goodman
Jimmie Davis

1. There's nothin' in the world that-'ll ev - er take the place of God's love,
2. I   start-ed out   trav'-lin' for the Lord man - y years   a- go,

Sil- ver and   gold could never buy His   love from above; When my
I've had a lot - ta heartache, met a lot - ta grief   and woe; And

soul needs heal - in' and I be - gin to feel - in' His pow'r,   I can
when I would stumble   Then I would   hum - ble down, And

say "thank the Lord, I would-n't take noth-in' for my jour-ney now."
there I would say   I would-n't take noth-in' for my jour-ney now.

CHORUS

Well, I would-n't take noth-in' for my journey now,   I've got-ta make it to

I Wouldn't Take Nothin' For My Journey

heav'n somehow; Though the devil tempts me and tries to turn me around; He's

of-fered ev-'ry-thing that's got a name, All the wealth I want and worldly fame; If I

could, still I would-n't take noth-in' for my jour-ney now.

67 P. P. B.   **Almost Persuaded**   P. P. Bliss

1. "Al-most per-suad-ed," Now to be-lieve; "Al-most per-suad-ed,"
2. "Al-most per-suad-ed," Come, come to-day; "Al-most per-suad-ed,"
3. "Al-most per-suad-ed," Har-vest is past; "Al-most per-suad-ed,"

Christ to re-ceive. Seems now some soul to say; "Go, Spir-it,
Turn not a-way. Je-sus in-vites you here, An-gels are
Doom comes at last. "Al-most" can-not a-vail; "Al-most" is

go Thy way, Some more con-ven-ient day, On Thee I'll call."
ling-'ring near, Pray'rs rise from hearts so dear, O wan-d'rer come!
but to fail, Sad, sad, that bit-ter wail; "Al-most, but lost!"

Do Lord

Traditional

Arr. for John T. Benson, Jr.

1. I've got a home in glo-ry land that out-shines the sun, I've got a home in
2. I took Jesus as my Sav-iour, you take Him too, I took Je-sus

glo-ry land that outshines the sun, I've got a home in glo-ry land that
as my Saviour, you take Him, too, I took Je-sus as my Saviour,

CHORUS

out-shines the sun, Way be-yond the blue. Do Lord, O do Lord, O
you take Him, too While He's call-ing you.

do re-mem-ber me, Do Lord, O do Lord, O do re-mem-ber me.

Do Lord, O do Lord, O do re-mem-ber me Way beyond the blue.

69 Kneel At The Cross

Words and Melody by Chas. E. Moody

Arr. for J. T. B. Pub. Co.

1. Kneel at the cross, Christ will meet you there, Come while He waits for you;
2. Kneel at the cross, There is room for all Who would His glo - ry share;
3. Kneel at the cross, Give your i - dols up, Look un - to realms a - bove;

List to His voice, Leave with Him your care And be - gin life a - new
Bliss there a - waits, Harm can ne'er be - fall Those who are anchored there.
Turn not a - way To life's sparkling cup, Trust on - ly in His love.

CHORUS

Kneel............ at the cross,...... ...... Leave....... ..
Kneel at the cross, Kneel at the cross, Leave ev - 'ry care

ev - 'ry care;............. .... Kneel............. at the
Leave ev - 'ry care; Kneel at the cross,

cross .... Je - sus will meet you there... ....
Kneel at the cross, meet you there.

Were You There

Arranged for John T. Benson Publishing Co.

1. Were you there when they cru-ci-fied my Lord? (were you there?)
2. Were you there when they nailed Him to the tree? (to the tree?)
3. Were you there when they pierced Him in the side? (in the side?)
4. Were you there when the sun re-fused to shine? (were you there?)
5. Were you there when they laid Him in the tomb? (in the tomb?)

Were you there when they cru-ci-fied my Lord? Oh!.......
Were you there when they nailed Him to the tree? Oh!.......
Were you there when they pierced Him in the side? Oh!.......
Were you there when the sun re-fused to shine? Oh!.......
Were you there when they laid Him in the tomb? Oh!.......

Some-times it caus-es me to trem-ble, trem-ble,
Some-times it caus-es me to trem-ble, trem-ble,
Some-times it caus-es me to trem-ble, trem-ble,
Some-times it caus-es me to trem-ble, trem-ble,
Some-times it caus-es me to trem-ble, trem-ble,

trem-ble, Were you there when they cru-ci-fied my Lord?
trem-ble, Were you there when they nailed Him to the tree?
trem-ble, Were you there when they pierced Him in the side?
trem-ble, Were you there when the sun re-fused to shine?
trem-ble, Were you there when they laid Him in the tomb?

71 Where We'll Never Grow Old

J. C. M.

To my Father and Mother.—J. C. M.
Jas. C. Moore, owner.

Jas. C. Moore

1. I have heard of a land on the far a-way strand, 'Tis a beau-ti-ful
2. In that beau-ti-ful home where we'll never-more roam, We shall be in the
3. When our work here is done and the life-crown is won, And our troubles and

home of the soul; Built by Je-sus on high, there we nev-er shall die,
sweet by and by; Hap-py praise to the King thru e-ter-ni-ty sing,
tri-als are o'er; All our sor-rows will end and our voic-es will blend,

CHORUS

'Tis a land where we nev-er grow old. Nev-er grow old,
'Tis a land where we nev-er shall die.
With the loved ones who've gone on be-fore. Where we'll

Nev-er grow old, In a land where we'll nev-er grow old; Nev-er grow

old. nev-er grow old, In a land where we'll nev-er grow old.
Where we'll

Peace In The Valley

T. A. D.   Thomas A. Dorsey

1. Well,   I'm tired and   so wea - ry,   but   I must go   a - long;
2. There   the flow'rs will   be bloom - ing,   and   the grass will   be green;
3. Well,   the bear will   be gen - tle,   and   the wolf will   be tame;

Till   the Lord comes   and calls   me   a - way,   oh,   yes;
And   the skies   will   be clear   and   serene,   oh,   yes;
And   the li - on shall   lay down   by   the lamb,   oh,   yes;

Well   the morn - ing   is bright,   and   the Lamb is   the Light;
Well   the sun ev - er beams,   in   this val - ley   of dreams;
Well   the beast from   the wild,   shall   be led by   a lit'le child;

And   the night,   night is as fair   as the   day,   oh, yes.
And   no clouds there   will ev - er   be   seen,   oh, yes.
And I'll be changed, changed from this creature that   I   am   oh, yes.

CHORUS

There will   be peace in   the val - ley   for   me   some day;

Peace In The Valley

There will be peace in the val-ley for me, oh, Lord, I pray;

There'll be no sad-ness, no sor-row, no trou-ble
no oh, my Lord-y no

I'll see; There will be peace in the val-ley for me.
trou-ble I'll for me.

73   A Charge To Keep I Have

CHARLES WESLEY.   LOWELL MASON.

1. A charge to keep I have, A God to glo - ri - fy,
2. To serve the pres - ent age, My call - ing to ful - fill,—
3. Arm me with jeal - ous care, As in Thy sight to live;
4. Help me to watch and pray, And on Thy - self re - ly,

A nev - er - dy - ing soul to save, And fit it for the sky.
Oh, may it all my pow'rs en - gage To do my Mas - ter's will.
And, oh, Thy serv - ant, Lord, pre - pare A strict ac - count to give.
As - sured, if I my trust be - tray, I shall for - ev - er die.

74

Unworthy

I. F. S.

Ira F. Stanphill

1. Un-wor-thy am I of the grace that He gave, Un-wor-thy to
2. My sor-row and sick-ness laid stripes on His back, My sins caused the
3. Un-wor-thy am I of the glo-ry to come, Un-wor-thy with

hold to His hand. Amazed that a King would reach down to a slave,
blood that was shed. My faults and my fail-ures have wov-en a crown
an-gels to sing. I thrill just to know that He loved me so much.

This love I can-not un-der-stand.
Of thorns, that He wore on His head. Un-wor-thy, un-
A pau-per, I walk with the King.

wor-thy, a beg-gar, In bond-age and a-lone- But He made me

wor-thy and now by His grace, His mer-cy has made me His own.

He's Got The Whole World In His Hands

Arr. by John T. Benson, Jr.

CHORUS

He's got the whole *wide* world   in His hands, He's got the whole *wide* world

in His hands, He's got the whole *wide* world,   in His hands, He's got the whole world

in His hands. He's got the wind   and the rain   in His hands; He's got the
in His hands. He's got the · sin-ner   man,   in His hands; He's got the
in His hands. He's got the ti-ny lit-tle ba-by in His hands; He's got the
in His hands. He's got   you   and   me   in His hands; He's got

wind   and the rain,   In His hands, He's got the wind   and the rain,
sin-ner   man;   In His hands, He's got the sin-ner   man,
ti-ny lit-tle ba-by;   In His hands, He's got the ti-ny lit-tle ba-by,
you   and   me;   In His hands, He's got   you   and   me,

4th and final ending

In His hands, He's got the whole world in His hands, whole world in His hands.

*Optional

Hide Thou Me

L. R. Tolbert

Thoro Harris

1. Some-times I feel dis-cour-aged, and think my life in vain,
2. Some-times it seems I dare not go one step far-ther on,
3. O what a Friend is Je-sus, sure An-chor for my soul.

I'm tempt-ed then to mur-mur, and of my lot com-plain;
And from my heart all cour-age has dis-ap-peared and gone;
So ten-der, true and gra-cious, I'm safe in His con-trol.

But when I think of Je-sus, and all He's done for me.
But, I re-mem-ber Je-sus, and all His love for me.
My help in time of dan-ger, my strong de-fense is He.

Then, I cry, O Rock of A-ges, Hide Thou me.
Then, I cry, O Rock of A-ges, Hide Thou me.
O Thou bless-ed Rock of A-ges, Hide Thou me.

CHORUS

O Rock of A-ges, Hide Thou me, No oth-er Ref-uge,

Hide Thou Me

have I but Thee, When life's dark vale I wan - der, Far, far from

Thee; Then, I cry, O Rock of A - ges, Hide Thou me.

O Come, Angel Band

Jefferson Hascall

W. B. Bradbury

1 { My lat - est sun is sink - ing fast, My race is near - ly run,
My strong - est tri - als now are past, My tri - umph is be - gun!

2 { I know I'm near - ing ho - ly ranks Of friends and kin - dred dear;
I brush the dew of Jordan's banks, The cross - ing must be near;

3 { I've al - most gained my heav'n - ly home, My spir - it loud - ly sings;
The ho - ly ones, be - hold, they come! I hear the noise of wings,

4 { O bear my long - ing heart to Him Who bled and died for me;
Whose blood now clean - ses from all sin, And gives me vic - to - ry.

Refrain f

O come, an - gel band, come, and around me stand, O bear me a - way on your

1. snow - y wings To my im - mor - tal home 2. my im - mor - tal home.

He Included Me

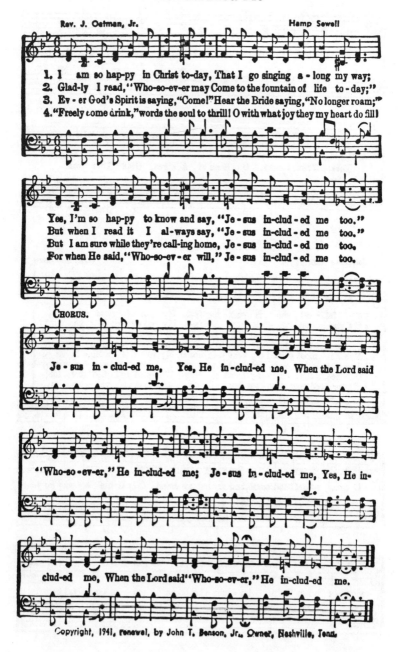

Rev. J. Oetman, Jr.　　　　　　　　　Hamp Sewell

1. I am so hap-py in Christ to-day, That I go singing a - long my way;
2. Glad-ly I read, "Who-so-ev-er may Come to the fountain of life to-day;"
3. Ev - er God's Spirit is saying, "Come!" Hear the Bride saying, "No longer roam;"
4. "Freely come drink," words the soul to thrill! O with what joy they my heart do fill!

Yes, I'm so hap-py to know and say, "Je - sus in-clud-ed me too."
But when I read it I al-ways say, "Je - sus in-clud-ed me too."
But I am sure while they're call-ing home, Je - sus in-clud-ed me too.
For when He said, "Who-so-ev - er will," Je - sus in-clud-ed me too.

CHORUS.

Je - sus in - clud-ed me, Yes, He in - clud-ed me, When the Lord said

"Who-so-ev-er," He in-clud-ed me; Je - sus in - clud-ed me, Yes, He in-

clud-ed me, When the Lord said "Who-so-ev-er," He in-clud-ed me.

O That Will Be Glory

C. H. G.   Chas. H. Gabriel

1. When all my la-bors and tri-als are o'er, And I am safe on that
2. When, by the gift of His in-fi-nite grace, I am ac-cord-ed in
3. Friends will be there I have loved long a-go, Joy like a riv-er a-

beau-ti-ful shore; Just to be near the dear Lord I a-dore,
heav-en a place; Just to be there and to look on His face, Will thru the
round me will flow; Yet, just a smile from my Sav-ior, I know,

a-ges be glo-ry for me.

CHORUS Faster

O that will be glo-ry for
O that will be

me, Glo-ry for me, glo-ry for me; When by His grace
glo-ry for me, Glo-ry for me, glo-ry for me;

I shall look on His face, That will be glo-ry, be glo-ry for me.

80 The Keys To The Kingdom

J. L. C.   Jenny Lou Carson

1. You hold the keys to the kingdom of God, Use them now, friend, and
2. Don't lose your keys to the kingdom of God, For you can't buy your

when you be-gin, Start with the key that will un-lock your heart,
way to the fold, Lov-eth thy neigh-bor, for love is the key

O-pen up and let Je-sus come in; The mas-ter key's next, my dear
To that heav-en-ly man-sion of gold; When trumpets ring out in the

neigh-bor, It's one you should use ev-'ry day, Prayer is the
morn-ing, And you step where an-gels have trod, That's the great

key to the great pearly gates, Yes, you're unlock-ing them when you pray.
day, you'll be so glad you used All the keys to the kingdom of God.

81 I Won't Have to Cross Jordan Alone

Thomas Ramsey

Chas. E. Durham

1. When I come to the riv-er at end-ing of day, When the last winds of
2. Of-ten-times I'm for-sak-en, and wea-ry and sad, When it seems that my
3. Tho' the bil-lows of sor-row and trouble may sweep, Christ the Sav-iour will

1. When the last

sor-row have blown; There'll be some-bod-y wait-ing to show me the way,
friends have all gone; There is one tho't that cheers me and makes my heart glad,
care for His own; Till the end of the jour-ney, my soul He will keep,

winds of sor-row have blown;

CHORUS

I won't have to cross Jor-dan a - lone.
I won't have to cross Jor-dan a-
I won't have to cross

lone. . . . Je-sus died for my sins to a - tone; When the
Jor-dan a-lone,

Solo ad lib.

PARTS

dark-ness I see, He'll be waiting for me, I won't have to cross Jordan a-lone.

Hum   Hum

I See Jesus

C. B. W.

Charles B. Wycuff

1. Once a man named Ste - phen, preached a - bout the Lord,
2. As the stones fell on him, beat - ing out his life,
3. Thro' the gates of glo - ry, down the streets of gold,

Folks were saved and folks were healed, As they heard his word;
Ste - phen knew he'd soon be thro', with all toil and strife;
Marched a he - ro of the Lord, In - to heav - ens fold;

Sa - tan did not like it, soon he had his crowd,
So much like the mas - ter, with a heart so true,
When he met the Sav - ior, at the great white throne,

And as he was tried they heard Ste - phen cry a - loud.
He prayed "Lord for - give for they know not what they do"
I be - lieve He smiled and said, "Ste - phen wel - come home"

CHORUS

"I see Je - sus, stand - ing at the Fa - ther's right hand,

I See Jesus

I see Je-sus, yon-der in the prom-ised land;

Work is o-ver, Now I'm com-ing to thee,

I see Je-sus, stand-ing wait-ing for me."

83   America

Samuel Francis Smith

Henry Carey

1. My coun-try 'tis of thee, Sweet land of liberty, Of thee I sing; Land where my fathers
2. My na-tive country thee, Land of the noble free, Thy name I love, I love thy rocks and
3. Let music swell the breeze, And ring from all the trees Sweet freedom's song; Let mortal tongues a-
4. Our father's God to thee, Author of liberty, To Thee we sing; Long may our land be

died, Land of the pilgrim's pride, From ev'ry   mountain side, Let   freedom ring.
rills, Thy woods and templed hills, My heart with rapture thrills, Like   that a-bove.
wake, Let all that breathe partake, Let rocks their silence break, The   sound prolong.
bright With freedom's holy light; Protect us   by Thy might, Great   God, our King.

I'll Meet You By The River

Dedicated to the memory of E. M. Bartlett, Sr.
Copyright, 1942, by Stamps-Baxter Music & Ptg. Co.
In "Lasting Peace"

A. E. B.   Albert E. Brumley

I'll Meet You By The River

Bright and shin-ing riv-er ... so far a-way;
By the bright and shin-ing riv-er ... far a-way;

Af-ter we have flown these prison bars to a ci-ty far be-yond the stars,

Meet you by the riv-er some sweet day.
I'll meet you by the riv-er ... some hap-py day.

85   Doxology

Thomas Ken   Louis Bourgeois

Praise God, from whom all bless-ings flow; Praise Him, all creatures here be-low;

Praise Him a-bove, ye heav'n-ly host; Praise Fa-ther, Son, and Ho-ly Ghost.

86

It Was Love

W. E. M.   W. Elmo Mercer

1. It was love that saved me, Won-drous, match-less
2. It was love that brought me Out of sin and
3. 'Twas the love of Je - sus Made my man - sion

love; So di - vine, so deep and wide,
shame; Gave me peace and hap - pi - ness,
fair; Some day ev - er - last - ing life,

CHORUS

Sent from heav'n a - bove. It was love, my
Washed a - way the stain.
With my Lord I'll share.

Sav - iour's love, How it fills my long - ings!

And I know this love is mine, Ev - 'ry - where I go.

Blessed Redeemer

AVIS BURGESON CHRISTIANSEN

Harry Dixon Loes

1. Up Cal-vary's mountain one dreadful morn, Walked Christ my Saviour, weary and worn;
2. "Fa-ther, forgive them!" thus did He pray, E'en while His life-blood flowed fast a-way;
3. O how I love Him, Sav-iour and Friend, How can my prais-es ev - er find end!

Fac-ing for sin-ners death on the cross, That He might save them from endless loss.
Pray-ing for sin-ners while in such woe— No one but His Je - sus' ev - er loved so.
Thro' years un-num-bered on heaven's shore, My tongue shall praise Him for-ev-er-more.

CHORUS

Bless-ed Re-deem - er! pre-cious Re-deem - er! Seems now I
Bless-ed Re-deem-er! bless - ed Re-deem - er!

see Him on Cal-va-ry's tree; Wound-ed and bleed - ing, for sin-ners
Wound-ed and bleed-ing,

plead - ing— Blind and un-heed - - ing— dy-ing for me!
for sin-ners plead - ing— Blind and un-heed - ing—

I'm-Bound For That City

Words and Music by Albert Brumley and
the Brumley Bros. Bill, Tom, Bob, Jack

1. There's a cit - y of light, Where there com - eth no night, For the sun
2. Lit - tle chil - dren will play, And our hearts will be gay, As we stroll

nev - er sets in the sky;........ In the Bi - ble we're told, that the
thru that cit - y of gold;........ No more dy - ing up there, no more

streets are pure gold, And a cool gen - tle riv - er runs
sor - row to bear, And no - bod - y will be fee - ble and

CHORUS

by. (riv - er runs by.) I'm bound for that cit - y God's ho - ly
old. (fee - ble and old.)

white cit - y, O yes, I am. I'll nev - er turn

I'm Bound For That City

back to this world an - y more; No mat - ter how

an - y more;

rough may be the way, No mat - ter how oft I stop to pray,

I'm bound for that cit - y, on that ev - er green shore.

ev - er green shore.

89   Amazing Grace

Rev. John Newton   Wm. Walker

1. A - maz - ing grace, how sweet the sound, That saved a wretch like me!
2. 'Twas grace that taught my heart to fear, And grace my fears re - lieved;
3. Thru man - y dan - gers, toils and snares, I have al - read - y come;
4. When we've been there ten thousand years, Bright shin - ing as the sun;

I once was lost but now I'm found, Was blind and now I see.
How pre-cious did that grace ap-pear The hour I first be-lieved.
'Tis grace has bro't me safe thus far, And grace will lead me home.
We've no less days to sing God's praise Than when we first be - gun.

I'm Looking For Jesus

W. L.

Wansley Lee

1. I can hard-ly wait to see my man-sion up on high, If I live
2. God said just to trust in Him and He would see you thru, When He comes

for Him each day, I know that by and by, When the Lord shall come
we'll trade this bod-y for one that is new; I'll not turn a-round

to take His chil-dren to the sky, I'll live and nev-er die.
be-cause for Him I'll be so true; My love will nev-er die.

CHORUS

I'm look-ing for Him to come some hap-py day,
I'm look-ing for Je-sus to come some day,

I'll ev-er keep sing-ing on my pil-grim way;
I'll ev-er keep sing-ing a-long my way,

I'm Looking For Jesus

heav-en's un-fold,   streets of pure gold,
Now when the heav-en's   un-fold, I'll walk the streets of   pure gold,

For Him to come some day.
I'm look-ing for Je-sus   to come some day.

91 ## Just A Rose Will Do

Arr. Copyright, 1948, by The Hartford Music Co., owners of original
in "Golden Gates"

J. A. McC.   J. A. McClung

1. When time shall come for my leav-ing, When I bid you a-dieu;
2. Just have an old-fash-ioned preacher Preach a ser-mon so true;
3. I'll need no or-gan-i-za-tion Just to make a "to-do;"

FINE

Don't spend your mon-ey for flow-ers, Just a rose will do.
I'll need no beau-ti-ful flow-ers, Just a rose will do.
I'll need no bright dec-o-ra-tions, Just a rose will do.

D. S.-Don't spend your mon-ey for flow-ers, Just a rose will do.

CHORUS   **D.S.**

I'll go to a beau-ti-ful gar-den, At last when life's work is thru;

I Can Call Jesus Anytime

Arrangment by Brock Speer

1. When I get in trou - ble fight - ing for the right,
2. When the storm is rag - ing, and the bil - lows roll,

Well, you know, I can call Je - sus an - y

time; When I feel dis - cour - aged He will lead me
When my heart is heav - y and my spir - its

on, I can call Je - sus an - y
low, Well, you know,

time.

CHORUS

You know, I can call
I can call Je - sus,

I Can Call Jesus Anytime

I Was There When It Happened

Mrs. R. D. Jones
Jimmie Davis

1. There are some peo-ple who say we can-not tell
2. Now I don't care who tells me sal-va-tion is not real,

Wheth-er we are saved, or, whether all is well; They say we on-ly can
Tho' the world may ar-gue that we can-not feel The heav-y bur - den

hope, and trust that it is so, But I was there when it
lift - ed and the vile sin go,

Solo
CHORUS

Yes, I know when Jesus

happened and I guess I ought to know (ought to know.)

I Was There When It Happened

saved me, The ve - ry moment He forgave me, He took a-

Yes, He saved my soul, And He made me whole,

way my heavy burden, He gave me peace within; Satan can't make me

Yes, He took my sin, Gave sweet peace within;

doubt it, It's real and I'm gon-na shout it

He can't make me doubt it, that's why I'm a gon-na

For I was there when it happened and I guess I ought to know.

shout it, Oh, my Lord Yes, I ought to know.

If We Never Meet Again

A. E. B.

Albert E. Brumley

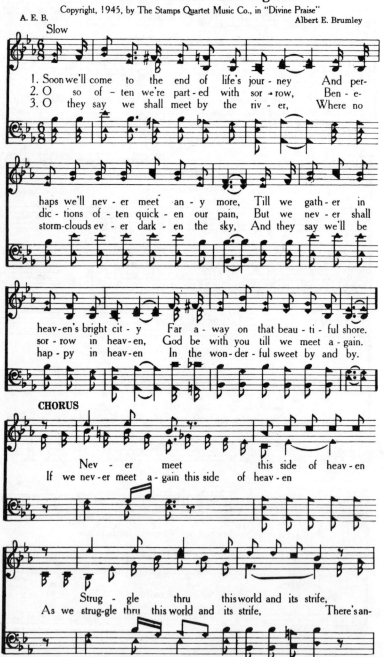

1. Soon we'll come to the end of life's jour-ney And per-
2. O so of-ten we're part-ed with sor-row, Ben-e-
3. O they say we shall meet by the riv-er, Where no

haps we'll nev-er meet an-y more, Till we gath-er in
dic-tions of-ten quick-en our pain, But we nev-er shall
storm-clouds ev-er dark-en the sky, And they say we'll be

heav-en's bright cit-y Far a-way on that beau-ti-ful shore.
sor-row in heav-en, God be with you till we meet a-gain.
hap-py in heav-en In the won-der-ful sweet by and by.

CHORUS

Nev-er meet this side of heav-en
If we nev-er meet a-gain this side of heav-en

Strug-gle thru this world and its strife,
As we strug-gle thru this world and its strife, There's an-

If We Never Meet Again

Meet - ing place somewhere in heav - en
oth - er meet - ing place somewhere in heav - en By the

By the shin - ing riv - er of life; Ros - es bloom
side of the riv - er of life; Where the charming ros - es bloom for-

ev - er and ev - er, Sep - a - ra - tions
ev - er, And where sep - a - ra - tions come no

come nev - er more, Nev - er meet
more, If we nev - er meet a - gain this side of

this side of heav-en, Meet you on that beau-ti - ful shore.
heav-en, I will meet you on that beau-ti-ful shore.

95

When I Stand With God

J. M.   John Mathews

Slowly

When I stand with God   no rag-ing storms   can ev-er shake me,
Hum   Hum

When I stand with Him   the cares of life   can't ev-er break me; For when I'm
Hum   Hum

cry-ing,   He dries my tears,   and when I'm frightened, He hides my fears,
Hum   Hum

All my sor-rows   dis-ap-pear   when I stand with Him.
Hum   Hum

CHORUS – Faster

When   I stand with Je-sus,   I will not fear
When I stand,   I   stand with Je-sus,   I'll not fear

When I Stand With God

the rag - ing tide, There'll be no lone - ly days of
the rag - ing tide, There will be no

sad - ness While we're stand - ing side by side;
days of sad - ness while we're stand - ing side by side;

Oh, just to hide with - in His bos - om when my
Just to hide with - in His bos - om

eyes are grow-ing dim; 'Twill be the an - swer
when my eyes are grow-ing dim; Be the an-

to all my prob-lems, When I stand with Him.
- swer, All my prob-lems, When I stand, I stand with Him.

96

I Know He Heard My Prayer

V. B. E.

V. B. (Vep) Ellis

1. The clouds have passed a-way, I see the light of day, The sun, in
2. The Lord has heard my prayer, great joy is now my share, Sweet heaven
3. When in the fu-ture days, the fi-ery tri-als blaze, When Sa-tan

shin-ing thru, dis-pel-ling gloom with hal-le-lu-jahs; I know that this is
fills my soul, now I can go re-joic-ing on; O my friend, there's not a
comes to me to take a-way my vic-to-ry, I can point him to the

real, for in my heart, I feel that my Sav-ior heard my ear-nest prayer.
doubt, thank God, they're driven out, for He heard my prayer, my earnest prayer.
time when heaven's light did shine, I can say He heard my ear-nest prayer.

CHORUS

I know He heard my prayer. He knows my ev-'ry care, He
Oh! I know He heard my prayer, and He knows my ev-'ry care,

gives to me the bless-ed vic-to-ry, O yes! I feel Him
Je-sus gives, gives to me vic-to-ry, blest vic-to-ry. Praise the Lord I

I Know He Heard My Prayer

now, My loy - al - ty I vow, I know the Savior heard my
feel Him now, loy-al-ty I to Him vow know the Lord heard my plea, I

plea. En - e - my had said to me, Satan said my
know He heard my plea. The en - e - my had said that my faith in God was

faith was dead. If the way was filled with care that the Savior
dead and if the way was rough He did not care.

did not care. Thank God it is not true, He thrills me thru and
Thank the Lord, it is not true, Je-sus thrills me

thru, I know He heard my prayer, my earnest prayer.
thru and thru, tru - ly know He heard my prayer, I know He heard my prayer.
earn - est prayer.

97   Jesus, Hold My Hand

Copyright assigned, 1944, to Albert E. Brumley

A. E. B.

Albert E. Brumley

1. As I trav-el thru this pil-grim land There is a Friend who
2. Let me trav-el in the light di-vine That I may see the
3. When I wan-der thru the val-ley dim To-ward the set-ting

walks with me, Leads me safe-ly thru the sink-ing sand, It is the
bless-ed way, Keep me that I may be whol-ly Thine And sing re-
of the sun, Lead me safe-ly to a land of rest, If I a

Christ of Cal-va-ry; This would be my pray'r, dear Lord, each
demption's song some day; I will be a sol-dier, brave and
crown of life have won; I have put my faith in Thee, dear

day To help me do the best I can, For I need Thy light to
true, and ev-er firm-ly take a stand, As I on-ward go and
Lord, That I may reach the gold-en strand, There's no oth-er friend on

guide me day and night, Bless - ed Je-sus, hold my hand.
dai - ly meet the foe, Bless - ed Je-sus, hold my hand.
whom I can de-pend, Bless - ed Je-sus, hold my hand.

Jesus, Hold My Hand

CHORUS

Je - sus, hold my hand, I need...... Thee ev - 'ry
Bless-ed Je - sus, hold my hand, Yes, I need Thee

hour, Thru...... this pil - grim land Pro-
ev - 'ry hour, Thru this land, this pil - grim land

tect me by Thy pow'r; Hear...... my fee - ble plea,
By Thy sav - ing pow'r; Hear my plea, my fee - ble plea,

O Lord,....... look down on me, When I kneel in
Lord, dear Lord, look down on me, When

pray'r I hope to meet you there, Bless - ed Je - sus, hold my hand.
kneel in pray'r,

I Can Tell You The Time

I Can Tell You The Time

I Want To Know More About My Lord

L. R. A.

Lee Roy Abernathy

1. While trav-'ling thru this world of sor-row, I'm on my way to glo-ry
2. I'm glad I know the bless-ed Sav-ior, For thru His blood He set me
3. He prom-ised when His soul as-cend-ed, I'm com-ing back, the Lord did

land; I'll not turn back, for some tomor-row, My tri-als here I'll un-der-
free; Tho rough the road, I shall not wav-er, For some glad day His face I'll
say; If on His prom-ise you've depend-ee, On wings of love you'll soar a-

CHORUS

stand. I want to know more about my Je-sus,
see.
way. I want to know more yes, I do,

I want to know more a-bout my Lord;
Yes, I want to know more my bless-ed Lord;

I want to know more about that man-sion,
I want to know more heaven-ly man-

I Want To Know More About My Lord

Just A Little While

E. M. B.

E. M. Bartlett

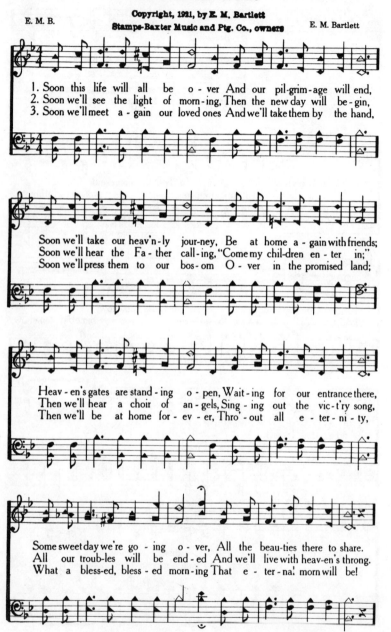

1. Soon this life will all be o-ver And our pil-grim-age will end,
2. Soon we'll see the light of morn-ing, Then the new day will be-gin,
3. Soon we'll meet a-gain our loved ones And we'll take them by the hand,

Soon we'll take our heav'n-ly jour-ney, Be at home a-gain with friends;
Soon we'll hear the Fa-ther call-ing, "Come my chil-dren en-ter in;"
Soon we'll press them to our bos-om O-ver in the promised land;

Heav-en's gates are stand-ing o-pen, Wait-ing for our entrance there,
Then we'll hear a choir of an-gels, Sing-ing out the vic-t'ry song,
Then we'll be at home for-ev-er, Thro'-out all e-ter-ni-ty,

Some sweet day we're go-ing o-ver, All the beau-ties there to share.
All our troub-les will be end-ed And we'll live with heav-en's throng.
What a bless-ed, bless-ed morn-ing That e-ter-nal morn will be!

Just A Little While

CHORUS

Just a lit-tle while to stay here, Just a lit-tle while to
stay here, stay here,

wait, Just a lit-tle while to la - bor In the path that's
to wait, la - bor, la - bor,

al - ways straight, Just a lit - tle more of
that's al-ways straight and narrow

trou - bles In this low and sin - ful state,
trou - bles, trou - bles, sin - ful state;

Then we'll en-ter heaven's por - tals, Sweeping thro' the pearl-y gates.
portals, por - tals, pearl-y gates.

101 When He Calls I'll Fly Away

Copyright 1943 by Tenn. Music & Printing Co., in "Songs of Rapture."

V. B. E.   V. B. (Vep) ELLIS

1. There was once a time when in my heart I was condemned to die,
2. I could nev-er think of turn-ing back in-to this world of sin,
3. If He needs me in His har-vest help-ing gath-er in the sheaves,

I was walk-ing in my sin-ful way (sin's way); Je-sus paid the
I'm re-joic-ing in this gos-pel way (this way); I am long-ing
I will glad-ly la-bor on be-low (be-low); If on earth my

ran-som for my soul, I bade the world good-bye, When He calls me
for the time when heav-en I shall en-ter in, I am read-y
work is fin-ished and it's time for me to leave, When He calls me

REFRAIN

I will fly a-way (a-way). When He calls me,
should He call to-day (to-day).
I'll be glad to go (to go).   When He calls me I will

I'm read-y

an-swer, "Here am I," I am read-y if He wants me to die;

When He Calls I'll Fly Away

There's a man-sion, I'm
There's a man-sion now a - wait-ing me on high,

go - ing there by - and - by, I have made my
by - and - by, I have made my

prep - a - ra - tion, from the world a
prep - a - ra - tion, from the world a sep - a -

sep - a - ra - tion, I am walk - ing on God's
ra - tion, I am walk - ing

highway, Calls I'll fly a - way.
on God's highway, When He calls I'll fly a - way.

O The Glory Did Roll

G. T. S.   G. T. Speer

1. I was kneel-ing one day,................ask-ing God to for-
2. I will praise His dear name................ for the won-der-ful

give me, hum-bly I prayed, I was deep in de-spair,................
vic-t'ry, down in my soul, And the joy in my heart................

had no peace with-in, had no peace with-in; I sur-ren-dered my
all a-long the way, all a-long the way; I am long-ing to

all................un-to Je-sus, the Sav-ior, bless His dear name,
see................heav-en's glo-ri-ous ci-ty, streets of pure gold,

Then the glo-ry came down............ I was saved from sin, I was saved from sin.
And to hear the Lord call, ... Come and live for aye, come and live for aye.

O The Glory Did Roll

Chorus

O the glo-ry did roll, I was hap-py and free;
O the glo-ry did roll,

I was hap-py and free; I had heard a sweet voice,
I had heard a sweet voice,

speak pardon to me; Such a won-der-ful joy
speak pardon to me; Such a won-der-ful

I was giv-en with-in, When the Sav-ior in
joy I was giv-en with-in, When the Sav-ior in love,

When the Sav-ior in love, saved me from all sin.
love, saved me from all sin.

Looking For A City

W. Oliver Cooper

Marvin P. Dalton

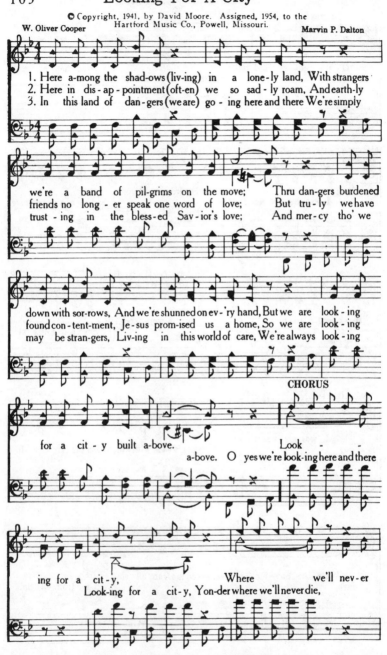

1. Here a-mong the shad-ows (liv-ing) in a lone-ly land, With strangers we're a band of pil-grims on the move; Thru dan-gers burdened down with sor-rows, And we're shunned on ev-'ry hand, But we are look-ing for a cit-y built a-bove.

2. Here in dis-ap-pointment (oft-en) we so sad-ly roam, And earth-ly friends no long-er speak one word of love; But tru-ly we have found con-tent-ment, Je-sus prom-ised us a home, So we are look-ing a-bove.

3. In this land of dan-gers (we are) go-ing here and there We're simply trust-ing in the bless-ed Sav-ior's love; And mer-cy tho' we may be stran-gers, Liv-ing in this world of care, We're always look-ing

CHORUS

Look - - O yes we're look-ing here and there ing for a cit-y, Where we'll nev-er Look-ing for a cit-y, Yon-der where we'll never die,

Looking For A City

die,   There   the sainted millions,
nev-er die no nev-er, And up there with all the saints,   yes, with all the millions,

Nev -   er say goodby,
We will nev-er say good-by,   say good-by no nev-er, Yes and

There   we'll meet our Savior,   And
when we gath - er there,   we'll meet Christ, our Savior, Glo-ry And we know we'll meet

our loved ones too,   Come   O ho - ly
friends and, all our loved ones, Now we pray Thee quickly come,

Spir-it,   All   our hopes renew.
Pray Thee come O spir - it, Come O come! on Thee we call,   All our hopes renew.

104 I'll Meet You In The Morning

Respectfully dedicated to my wife, Goldie, and my sons,
Billey Joe, Albert E. Jr. and Thomas Rexton—A. E. B.

A. E. B.

Copyright 1936 by Hartford Music Co. in "Lights of Life"

Albert E. Brumley

1. I will meet you in the morn-ing, by the bright riv-er side,
2. I will meet you in the morn-ing, in the sweet by and by,
3. I will meet you in the morn-ing, at the end of the way,

When all sor-row has drift-ed a-way; I'll be stand-ing at the
And exchange the old cross for a crown; There will be no dis-ap-
On the streets of that cit-y of gold; Where we all can be to-

por-tals, when the gates o-pen wide, At the close of life's long, dreary day.
pointments and no-bod-y shall die, In that land, when life's sun go-eth down.
geth-er and be hap-py for aye, While the years and the a-ges shall roll.

CHORUS

Meet you in the morn-ing, meet you in the morn-ing,
I'll meet . . . . you in the morn-ing, ...

"How do you do" "How do you do"
with a "How . . . . do you do" . . . . and we'll

I'll Meet You In The Morning

105

Heavenly Love

V. B. E.

Title suggested by Bill Baker, Louisville, Ky.

V. B. (Vep) Ellis

1. Heav - en - ly love............ was all that could help me,............ was a - stray............ so sad and a - lone;............ I looked a - bove............ my bur - dens all left me,............ Now I can say,............ "Heav-en's my home"............
2. Trou - bles of earth (repeat words of soprano) so of - ten o'er- take me,............ Bur - dens of life............ with heart - ache and care;............ Heav - en - ly love............ will nev - er for - sake me,............ Fill - ing my need,............ Je - sus is there............
3. When I shall stand............ at Jor - dan's dark riv - er,............ Shad - ows of night............ are gath - 'ring a - bove;............ There is a pow'r............ I know will de - liv - er,............ Heav - en - ly love,............ heav - en - ly love............

Heavenly Love

How Firm A Foundation

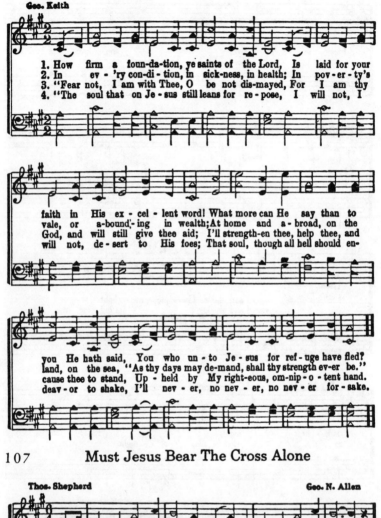

Geo. Keith

1. How firm a foun-da-tion, ye saints of the Lord, Is laid for your
2. In ev - 'ry con-di - tion, in sick-ness, in health; In pov-er-ty's
3. "Fear not, I am with Thee, O be not dis-mayed, For I am thy
4. "The soul that on Je - sus still leans for re - pose, I will not, I

faith in His ex - cel - lent word! What more can He say than to
vale, or a-bound-'-ing in wealth; At home and a - broad, on the
God, and will still give thee aid; I'll strength-en thee, help thee, and
will not, de - sert to His foes; That soul, though all hell should en-

you He hath said, You who un - to Je - sus for ref - uge have fled?
land, on the sea, "As thy days may de-mand, shall thy strength ev-er be."
cause thee to stand, Up - held by My right-eous, om-nip-o - tent hand.
deav - or to shake, I'll nev - er, no nev - er, no nev - er for - sake.

Must Jesus Bear The Cross Alone

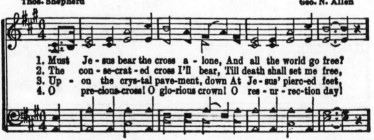

Thos. Shepherd   Geo. N. Allen

1. Must Je - sus bear the cross a - lone, And all the world go free?
2. The con - se-crat - ed cross I'll bear, 'Till death shall set me free;
3. Up - on the crys-tal pave-ment, down At Je - sus' pierc-ed feet,
4. O pre-cious cross! O glo-rious crown! O res - ur - rec-tion day!

Must Jesus Bear The Cross Alone

No, there's a cross for ev-'ry one, And there's a cross for me.
And then go home my crown to wear, For there's a crown for me.
With joy I'll cast my gold-en crown, And His dear name re-peat.
Ye an-gels from the stars come down And bear my soul a-way.

108   I Feel Like Traveling On

WM. HUNTER, D. D.   ARR. by JAMES D. VAUGHAN.
With feeling.

1. My heav-'nly home is bright and fair, I feel like trav-el-ing on,
2. Its glit-t'ring tow'rs the sun out-shine, I feel like trav-el-ing on,
3. Let oth-ers seek a home be-low, I feel like trav-el-ing on,
4. The Lord has been so good to me, I feel like trav-el-ing on,

Nor pain, nor death can en-ter there, I feel like travel-ing on.
That heav'nly mansion shall be mine, I feel like travel-ing on.
Which flames devour, or waves o'erflow, I feel like travel-ing on.
Un-til that bless-ed home I see, I feel like travel-ing on.

REFRAIN.

Yes, I feel like trav-el-ing on,   I feel like trav-el-ing
              trav-el-ing on,

on;   My heav'nly home is bright and fair, I feel like traveling on.
travel-ing on;

There Is A Fountain

William Cowper

Lowell Mason

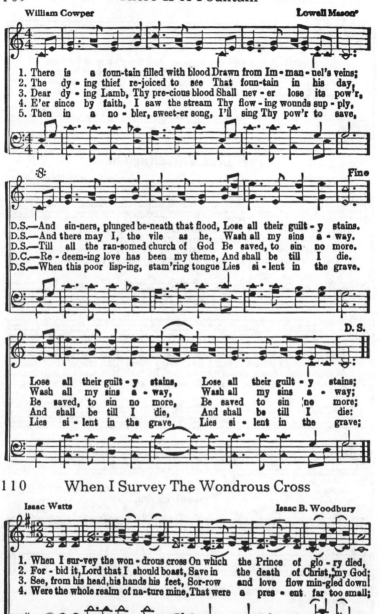

1. There is a foun-tain filled with blood Drawn from Im-man-uel's veins;
2. The dy-ing thief re-joiced to see That foun-tain in his day,
3. Dear dy-ing Lamb, Thy pre-cious blood Shall nev-er lose its pow'r,
4. E'er since by faith, I saw the stream Thy flow-ing wounds sup-ply,
5. Then in a no-bler, sweet-er song, I'll sing Thy pow'r to save,

Fine

D.S.—And sin-ners, plunged be-neath that flood, Lose all their guilt-y stains.
D.S.—And there may I, the vile as he, Wash all my sins a-way.
D.S.—Till all the ran-somed church of God Be saved, to sin no more.
D.C.—Re-deem-ing love has been my theme, And shall be till I die.
D.S.—When this poor lisp-ing, stam'ring tongue Lies si-lent in the grave.

D. S.

Lose all their guilt-y stains, Lose all their guilt-y stains;
Wash all my sins a-way, Wash all my sins a-way;
Be saved, to sin no more, Be saved to sin no more;
And shall be till I die, And shall be till I die:
Lies si-lent in the grave, Lies si-lent in the grave;

110 When I Survey The Wondrous Cross

Isaac Watts

Isaac B. Woodbury

1. When I sur-vey the won-drous cross On which the Prince of glo-ry died,
2. For-bid it, Lord that I should boast, Save in the death of Christ, my God:
3. See, from his head, his hands his feet, Sor-row and love flow min-gled down:
4. Were the whole realm of na-ture mine, That were a pres-ent far too small;

When I Survey The Wondrous Cross

My rich-est gain I count but loss, And pour con-tempt on all my pride.
All the vain things that charm me most I sac - ri - fice them to his blood.
Did e'er such love and sor-row meet, Or thorns com-pose so rich a crown?
Love so a-maz-ing, so di - vine, De-mands my soul, my life, my all.

111 Surrender All

"But as for me and my house, we will serve the Lord."—Josh. 24: 15.

J. W. Van De Venter. DUET. W. S. Weeden.

1. { All to Je - sus I sur-ren - der, All to Him I free-ly give;
{ I will ev - er love and trust Him, In His pres-ence dai - ly live.
2. { All to Je - sus I sur-ren - der, Hum-bly at His feet I bow,
{ World-ly pleasures all for-sak - en, Take me, Je - sus, take me now.
3. { All to Je - sus I sur-ren - der, Make me, Sav-iour, whol-ly thine;
{ Let me feel the Ho - ly Spir - it, Tru - ly know that Thou art mine.
4. { All to Je - sus I sur-ren - der, Lord, I give my-self to Thee;
{ Fill me with Thy love and pow - er, Let Thy bless-ing fall on me.
5. { All to Je - sus I sur-ren - der, Now I feel the sa - cred flame;
{ O the joy of full sal - va - tion! Glo - ry, glo - ry to His name.

CHORUS.

I sur-ren - der all, I sur-ren - der all,
I sur-ren-der all, I sur-ren-der all,
All to Thee, my bless - ed Sav - iour, I sur - ren - der all.

Johnson Oatman, Jr.

Geo. C. Hugg

1. There's not a friend like the low-ly Je-sus,
2. No friend like Him is so high and ho-ly,
3. There's not an hour that He is not near us, No, not one! no, not one!
4. Did ev-er saints find this Friend for-sake Him?
5. Was e'er a gift, like the Sav-ior giv-en?

None else could heal all our soul's dis-eas-es,
And yet no friend is so meek and low-ly,
No night so dark but His love can cheer us, No, not one, no, not one!
Or sin-ner find that He would not take him?
Will He re-fuse us a home in heav-en?

D.S.—There's not a friend like the low-ly Je-sus, No, not one, no, not one!

Chorus

Je-sus knows all a-bout our strug-gles, He will guide till the day is done,

---

113   I Am Bound For The Promised Land

Rev. Samuel Stennet

Rev. 21:2

Arr. by Rev. E. M. Parnum

1. On Jor-dan's storm-y banks I stand, And cast a wish-ful eye,
2. O'er all those wide ex-tend-ed plains Shines one e-ter-nal day;
3. No chill-ing winds, nor pois'nous breath, Can reach that health-ful shore;
4. When shall I reach that hap-py place, And be for-ev-er blest!

Cho.—I am bound for the prom-ised land, I am bound for the promised land;

I Am Bound For The Promised Land

T'ward Ca-naan's fair and hap - py land, Where my pos - ses - sions lie.
There God the Son for - ev - er reigns, And scat - ters night a - way.
Sick - ness and sor - row, pain and death, Are feared and felt no more.
When shall I see my Fa-ther's face, And in His bos - om rest?

O who will come and go with me, I am bound for the promised land.

114 All Hail The Power

Edward Perronet   Oliver Holden

1. All hail the pow'r of Je - sus' name! Let an - gels pros-trate fall!
2. Ye cho - sen seed of Is - rael's race, Ye ran-somed from the fall,
3. Let ev - 'ry kin - dred, ev - 'ry tribe, On this ter - res - trial ball,
4. O that with yon - der sa - cred throng, We at His feet may fall!

Bring forth the roy - al di - a - dem,
Hail Him who saves you by His grace, And crown Him Lord of all!
To Him all maj - es - ty as - cribe,
We'll join the ev - er - last - ing song,

Bring forth the roy - al di - a - dem,
Hail Him who saves you by His grace, And crown Him Lord of all!
To Him all maj - es - ty as - cribe,
We'll join the ev - er - last - ing song,

Whiter Than Snow

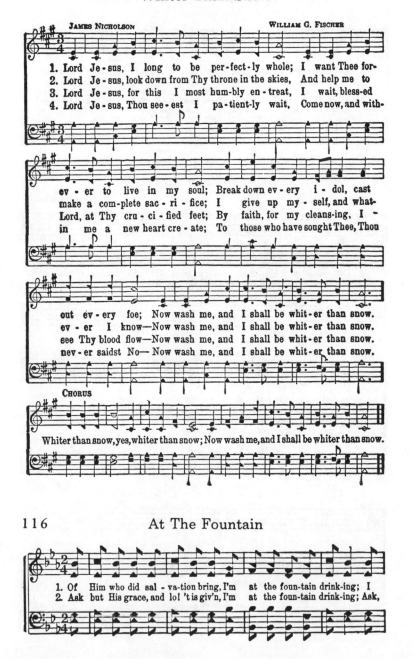

JAMES NICHOLSON

WILLIAM G. FISCHER

1. Lord Je-sus, I long to be per-fect-ly whole; I want Thee for-
2. Lord Je-sus, look down from Thy throne in the skies, And help me to
3. Lord Je-sus, for this I most hum-bly en-treat, I wait, bless-ed
4. Lord Je-sus, Thou see-est I pa-tient-ly wait, Come now, and with-

ev-er to live in my soul; Break down ev-ery i-dol, cast
make a com-plete sac-ri-fice; I give up my-self, and what-
Lord, at Thy cru-ci-fied feet; By faith, for my cleans-ing, I -
in me a new heart cre-ate; To those who have sought Thee, Thou

out ev-ery foe; Now wash me, and I shall be whit-er than snow.
ev-er I know—Now wash me, and I shall be whit-er than snow.
see Thy blood flow—Now wash me, and I shall be whit-er than snow.
nev-er saidst No— Now wash me, and I shall be whit-er than snow.

CHORUS

Whiter than snow, yes, whiter than snow; Now wash me, and I shall be whiter than snow.

116

At The Fountain

1. Of Him who did sal-va-tion bring, I'm at the foun-tain drink-ing; I
2. Ask but His grace, and lo! 't is giv'n, I'm at the foun-tain drink-ing; Ask,

At The Fountain

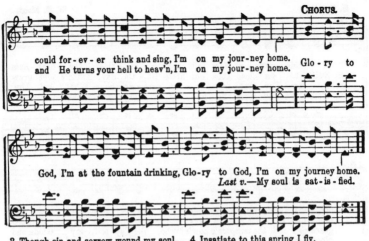

could for-ev-er think and sing, I'm on my jour-ney home. Glo-ry to
and He turns your hell to heav'n, I'm on my jour-ney home.

God, I'm at the fountain drinking, Glo-ry to God, I'm on my journey home.
Last v.—My soul is sat-is-fied.

3 Though sin and sorrow wound my soul,
   I'm at the fountain drinking;
Jesus, Thy balm will make it whole,
   I'm on my journey home.

4 Insatiate to this spring I fly,
   I'm at the fountain drinking;
I drink, and yet am ever dry,
   I'm on my journey home.

---

117   Come, Ye Sinners, Poor and Needy

JOSEPH HART.   Anon.

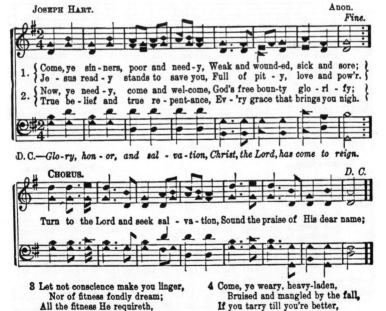

1. Come, ye sin-ners, poor and need-y, Weak and wound-ed, sick and sore;
   Je-sus read-y stands to save you, Full of pit-y, love and pow'r.

2. Now, ye need-y, come and wel-come, God's free boun-ty glo-ri-fy;
   True be-lief and true re-pent-ance, Ev-'ry grace that brings you nigh.

D.C.—*Glo-ry, hon-or, and sal-va-tion, Christ, the Lord, has come to reign.*

CHORUS.

Turn to the Lord and seek sal-va-tion, Sound the praise of His dear name;

3 Let not conscience make you linger,
   Nor of fitness fondly dream;
All the fitness He requireth,
   Is to feel your need of Him.

4 Come, ye weary, heavy-laden,
   Bruised and mangled by the fall,
If you tarry till you're better,
   You will never come at all.

Abide With Me

H. F. Lyte

W. H. Monk

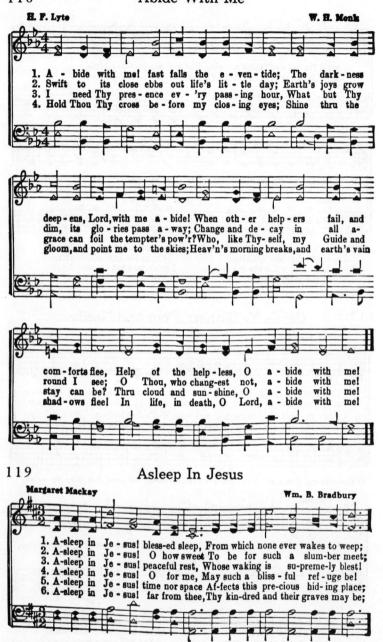

1. A - bide with me! fast falls the e - ven - tide; The dark - ness
2. Swift to its close ebbs out life's lit - tle day; Earth's joys grow
3. I need Thy pres - ence ev - 'ry pass - ing hour, What but Thy
4. Hold Thou Thy cross be - fore my clos - ing eyes; Shine thru the

deep - ens, Lord, with me a - bide! When oth - er help - ers fail, and
dim, its glo - ries pass a - way; Change and de - cay in all a -
grace can foil the tempter's pow'r? Who, like Thy- self, my Guide and
gloom, and point me to the skies; Heav'n's morning breaks, and earth's vain

com - forts flee, Help of the help - less, O a - bide with me!
round I see; O Thou, who chang-est not, a - bide with me!
stay can be? Thru cloud and sun - shine, O a - bide with me!
shad - ows flee! In life, in death, O Lord, a - bide with me!

Asleep In Jesus

Margaret Mackay

Wm. B. Bradbury

1. A-sleep in Je - sus! bless-ed sleep, From which none ever wakes to weep;
2. A-sleep in Je - sus! O how sweet To be for such a slum-ber meet;
3. A-sleep in Je - sus! peaceful rest, Whose waking is su-preme-ly blest!
4. A-sleep in Je - sus! O for me, May such a bliss - ful ref - uge be!
5. A-sleep in Je - sus! time nor space Af-fects this pre-cious hid-ing place;
6. A-sleep in Je - sus! far from thee, Thy kin-dred and their graves may be;

Asleep In Jesus

A calm and un-dis-turbed re-pose, Un-brok-en by the last of foes!
With ho-ly con-fi-dence to sing, That death has lost its ven-omed sting!
No fear, no woe, shall dim that hour That man-i-fests the Sav-ior's pow'r.
Se-cure-ly shall my ash-es lie, And wait the summons from on high.
On In-dian plains, on Lap-land snows, Be-liev-ers find the same re-pose.
But thine is still a bless-ed sleep, From which none ever wakes to weep.

120   Lead, Kindly Light

J. H. Newman   Rev. J. B. Dpkes

1 { Lead, kindly Light! a-mid th' encircling gloom, Lead Thou me on; }
  { The night is dark, and I am far from (Omit.....................) }

2 { I was not ev-er thus, nor pray'd that Thou Shouldst lead me on; }
  { I loved to choose and see my path; but (Omit.....................) }

3 { So long Thy pow'r has blessed me, sure it still Will lead me on }
  { O'er moor and fen, o'er crag and torrent, (Omit.....................) }

home, Lead Thou me on; Keep Thou my feet; I do not
now   Lead Thou me on; I loved the   gar - ish day, and
till   The night is gone; And with the morn those an-gel

ask to see The dis-tant scene; one step e-nough for me.
spite of fears, Pride ruled my will. Remember not past years.
fac - es smile, Which I have loved long since, and lost a-while!

121   Why Not Now

El Nathan.   C. C. Case.

1. While we pray, and while we plead, While you see your soul's deep need,
2. You have wandered far a-way; Do not risk an-oth-er day;
3. In the world you've failed to find Aught of peace for troub-led mind;
4. Come to Christ, con-fes-sion make; Come to Christ and par-don take;

While your Fa-ther calls you home, Will you not, my broth-er, come?
Do not turn from God your face, But, to-day, ac-cept His grace.
Come to Christ, on Him be-lieve, Peace and joy you shall re-ceive.
Trust in Him from day to day, He will keep you all the way.

CHORUS.

Why not now? Why not now? Why not come to Jesus now?
Why not now? why not now? Why not come to Je-sus now?

122   At The Cross

Isaac Watts   R. E. Hudson

1. A-las, and did my Sav-ior bleed, And did my Sov-ereign die; Would He de-
2. Was it for crimes that I have done, He groaned up-on the tree? A-maz-ing
3. Well might the sun in darkness hide, And shut His glo-ries in, When Christ, the
4. But drops of grief can ne're re-pay The debt of love I owe: Here, Lord, I

Chorus

vote that sa-cred head For such a worm as I?
pit-y, grace unknown! And love beyond degree! At the cross, at the cross where I
might-y Mak-er, died For man the creature's sin.
give my-self a-way, 'Tis all that I can do!

At The Cross

first saw the light, And the bur-den of my heart rolled a-way, It was
rolled a-way,

there by faith I re-ceived my sight, And now I am hap-py all the day!

123 Jesus Paid It All

Mrs. H. M. Hall

John T. Grape

1. I   hear the Sav-ior say, "Thy strength in-deed is small, Child of
2. Lord, now in-deed I find Thy pow'r, and Thine a-lone, Can
3. For   noth-ing good have I Where-by Thy grace to claim—I'll
4. And   when, be-fore the throne, I stand in Him com-plete, "Je-sus

Chorus

weakness watch and pray, Find in Me thine all in all."
change the lep-er's spots, And melt the heart of stone. Je-sus paid it all,
wash my garments white In the blood of Cal-v'ry's Lamb.
died my soul to save," "My lips shall still re-peat.

All to Him I owe; Sin had left a crimson stain, He washed it white as snow.

Softly And Tenderly

Will L. Thompson

1. Soft - ly and ten - der - ly Je - sus is call - ing, Call - ing for
2. Why should we tar - ry when Je - sus is plead - ing, Plead - ing for
3. Time now is fleet - ing, the mo - ments are pass - ing, Pass - ing from
4. O for the won - der - ful love He has prom - ised, Prom - ised for

you and for me, See on the por - tals He's wait - ing and watch - ing,
you and for me? Why should we lin - ger and heed not His mer - cies,
you and from me; Shad - ows are gath - er - ing, death beds are com - ing,
you and for me; Tho we have sinned He has mer - cy and par - don,

CHORUS

Watch - ing for you and for me. Come home, come
Mer - cies for you and for me?
Com - ing for you and for me.
Par - don for you and for me.

Come home,

home, Ye who are wea - ry, come home, Ear - nest - ly

come home,

ten - der - ly, Je - sus is call - ing, Call - ing, O sin - ner, come home.

W. L. T.   W. L. Thompson

1. There's a great day com-ing, a great day com-ing, There's a great day com-ing by and by, When the saints and the sin-ners shall be part - ed, right and left, Are you read-y for that day to come?

2. There's a bright day com-ing, a bright day com-ing, There's a bright day com-ing by and by, But its bright-ness shall on-ly come to them that love the Lord, Are you read-y for that day to come?

3. There's a sad day com-ing, a sad day com-ing, There's a sad day com-ing by and by, When the sin-ner shall hear his doom, "De-part, I know ye not,"

Chorus

Are you read-y, are you read-y? Are you read-y for the judg-ment day? Are you ready, are you read-y For the judg-ment day?

126 Only Trust Him

J. H. S.   J. H. Stockton

1. Come, ev - 'ry soul by sin op-pressed, There's mer-cy with the Lord,
2. For Je - sus shed His pre - cious blood, Rich bless-ings to be - stow;
3. Yes, Je - sus is the Truth, the Way, That leads you in - to rest;
4. Come, then, and join this ho - ly band, And on to glo - ry go,

And He will sure - ly give you rest By trust - ing in His word.
Plunge now in - to the crim - son flood That wash - es white as snow.
Be - lieve in Him with - out de - lay, And you are ful - ly blest.
To dwell in that ce - les - tial land, Where joys im - mor - tal flow.

Chorus

{ On - ly trust Him, on - ly trust Him, On-ly trust Him now; }
{ He will save you, He will save you, He will (Omit.......) } save you now.

127 Just As I Am

Charlotte Elliott   William B. Bradbury

1. Just as I am, with - out one plea, But that Thy blood was shed for me,
2. Just as I am, and wait - ing not To rid my soul of one dark blot,
3. Just as I am, tho tossed about With many a con-flict, many a doubt,
4. Just as I am, poor, wretched, blind; Sight, rich - es, heal-ing of the mind,
5. Just as I am—Thou wilt re-ceive, Wilt welcome, pardon, cleanse, relieve;

Just As I Am

And that Thou bidd'st me come to Thee, O Lamb of God, I come! I come!
To Thee whose blood can cleanse each spot, O Lamb of God, I come! I come!
Fight-ings and fears with-in, with-out, O Lamb of God, I come! I come!
Yea, all I need in Thee to find, O Lamb of God, I come! I come!
Be - cause Thy promise I be-lieve, O Lamb of God, I come! I come!

128   Pass Me Not

Fanny J. Crosby

W. H. Doane

1. Pass me not, O gen-tle Sav-ior, Hear my hum-ble cry; While on oth-ers
2. Let me at a throne of mer-cy Find a sweet re-lief; Kneel-ing there in
3. Trusting on-ly in Thy mer-it, Would I seek Thy face; Heal my wounded
4. Thou the Spring of all my com-fort, More than life to me, Whom have I on

Chorus

Thou art call-ing, Do not pass me by.
deep con-trition, Help my un-be-lief.   Sav-ior, Sav - ior, Hear my humble
brok-en spir-it, Save me by Thy grace.
earth beside Thee? Whom in heav'n but Thee?

cry; While on oth - ers Thou art call - ing, Do not pass me by.

W. J. K.   Wm. J. Kirkpatrick

1. I've wan-dered far a - way from God, Now I'm com-ing home;
2. I've wast - ed man - y pre - cious years, Now I'm com-ing home;
3. I'm tired of sin and stray - ing, Lord, Now I'm com-ing home;
4. My soul is sick, my heart is sore, Now I'm com-ing home;
5. My on - ly hope, my on - ly plea, Now I'm com-ing home;
6. I need His cleans-ing blood, I know, Now I'm com-ing home;

The paths of sin too long I've trod, Lord, I'm com-ing home.
I now re-pent with bit - ter tears, Lord, I'm com-ing home.
I'll trust Thy love, be - lieve Thy word, Lord, I'm com-ing home.
My strength re - new, my hope re - store, Lord, I'm com-ing home.
That Je - sus died, and died for me, Lord, I'm com-ing home.
O wash me whi - ter than the snow, Lord, I'm com-ing home.

CHORUS

Com - ing home, com - ing home, Nev - er - more to roam;

O - pen wide Thine arms of love, Lord, I'm com-ing home.

Fanny J. Crosby   George C. Stebbins

1. Je - sus is ten - der - ly call - ing thee home—Call - ing to - day,
2. Je - sus is call - ing the wea - ry to rest—Call - ing to - day,
3. Je - sus is wait - ing, O come to Him now—Wait - ing to - day,
4. Je - sus is plead - ing, O list to His voice—Hear Him to - day,

call - ing to - day; Why from the sun-shine of love wilt thou roam
call - ing to - day; Bring Him thy bur - den, and thou shalt be blest;
wait - ing to - day; Come with thy sins, at His feet low - ly bow;
hear Him to - day; They who be - lieve on His name shall re - joice;

Chorus

Far - ther and far - ther a - way?
He will not turn you a - way.   Call - ing to - day!
Come, and no lon - ger de - lay.   Call - ing, call - ing to - day, to - day!
Quick-ly a - rise and a - way.

Call - ing to - day!........   Je - sus is
Call - ing, call - ing to - day, to - day!   Je - sus is ten - der - ly

call - ing, Is ten - der - ly call - ing to - day.
call - ing to - day,

I Am Coming To The Cross

W. H. McDonald

Wm. G. Fischer

1. I am com-ing to the cross; I am poor and weak and blind;
2. Long my heart has sighed for Thee; Long has e - vil dwelt with-in;
3. Here I give my all to Thee Friends and time and earth - ly store,
4. In the prom-is - es I trust; Now I feel the blood ap - plied;

Cho.—I am trust-ing, Lord, in Thee, Dear Lamb of Cal - va - ry,

D. C. for Chorus

I am count - ing all but dross; I shall full sal - va - tion find.
Je - sus sweet - ly speaks to me, "I will cleanse you from all sin."
Soul and bod - y Thine to be Whol - ly Thine for - ev - er more.
I am pros - trate in the dust; I with Christ am cru - ci - fied.

Hum-bly at the cross I bow, Save me, Je - sus, save me now.

132 Glory To His Name

Rev. E. A. Hoffman

Rev. J. H. Stockton

1. Down at the cross where my Sav-ior died, Down where for cleansing from
2. I am so won - drous-ly saved from sin, Je - sus so sweet-ly a-
3. Oh, precious foun-tain that saves from sin, I am so glad I have
4. Come to this foun-tain so rich and sweet; Cast thy poor soul at the

Fine

sin I cried, There to my heart was the blood ap-plied; Glo-ry to His name.
bides with-in, There at the cross where He took me in; Glo-ry to His name.
en - tered in; There Je-sus saves me and keeps me clean; Glo-ry to His name.
Sav-ior's feet; Plunge in to - day and be made com-plete; Glo-ry to His name.

D. S., There to my heart was the blood ap-plied; Glo-ry to His name.

Glory To His Name

Chorus   **D. S.**

Glo - ry to His name, Glo - ry to His name;

133   Nothing But The Blood   Robert Lowry

R. L.

1. What can wash a - way my sins? Noth-ing but the blood of Je - sus;
2. For my par-don this I see, Noth-ing but the blood of Je - sus;
3. Noth-ing can for sin a - tone, Noth-ing but the blood of Je - sus;
4. This is all my hope and peace, Noth-ing but the blood of Je - sus;

What can make me whole a - gain? Noth-ing but the blood of Je - sus.
For my cleans-ing, this my plea, Noth-ing but the blood of Je - sus.
Naught of good that I have done, Noth-ing but the blood of Je - sus.
This is all my right-eous-ness, Noth-ing but the blood of Je - sus.

Chorus

Oh! pre - cious is the flow That makes me white as snow;

No oth - er fount I know, Noth-ing but the blood of Je - sus.

134 Where He Leads Me

E. W. Blandly

J. S. Norris

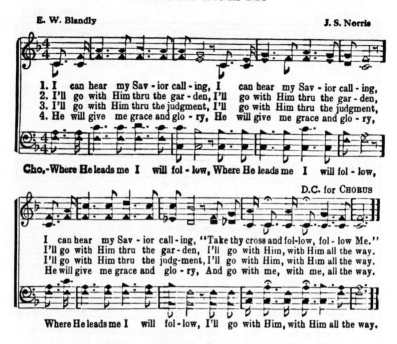

1. I can hear my Sav-ior call-ing, I can hear my Sav-ior call-ing,
2. I'll go with Him thru the gar-den, I'll go with Him thru the gar-den,
3. I'll go with Him thru the judgment, I'll go with Him thru the judgment,
4. He will give me grace and glo-ry, He will give me grace and glo-ry,

Cho.-Where He leads me I will fol-low, Where He leads me I will fol-low,

D.C. for Chorus

I can hear my Sav-ior call-ing, "Take thy cross and fol-low, fol-low Me."
I'll go with Him thru the gar-den, I'll go with Him, with Him all the way.
I'll go with Him thru the judg-ment, I'll go with Him, with Him all the way.
He will give me grace and glo-ry, And go with me, with me, all the way.

Where He leads me I will fol-low, I'll go with Him, with Him all the way.

135 Jesus Breaks Every Fetter

Old Melody.

1. I am all on the al-tar, I am all on the al-tar,
2. He ac-cepts all I've brought Him, He ac-cepts all I've brought Him,
3. I will nev-er-more doubt Him, I will nev-er-more doubt Him,
4. I will rest on His prom-ise, I will rest on His prom-ise,
5. Hal-le-lujah! I will praise Him, Hal-le-lujah I will praise Him,

Cho.-Je-sus breaks ev-'ry fet-ter, Je-sus breaks ev-'ry fet-ter,

I am all on the al-tar; Which was made for me.
He ac-cepts all I've brought Him; And that's e-ven me.
I will nev er-more doubt Him; For He cleans-es me.
I will rest on His prom-ise; Which was made for me.
Ha-le-lujah! I will praise Him; For He sets me free.

Je-sus breaks ev-'ry fet-ter, Je-sus sets me free.

Oh, Why Not Tonight

J. Calvin Bushey.

1. Oh, do not let the world de - part, And close thine eyes against the light;
2. To - mor-row's sun may nev-er rise, To bless thy long de - lud - ed sight;
3. Our Lord in pit - y lin-gers still, And wilt thou thus His love re - quite?
4. Our bless - ed Lord re - fus - es none Who would to Him their souls u - nite;

Poor sin - ner, hard - en not your heart, Be saved, oh, to - night.
This is the time, oh, then be wise, Be saved, oh, to - night.
Re - nounce at once thy stub - born will, Be saved, oh, to - night.
Be - lieve, o - bey, the work is done, Be saved, oh, to - night.

Chorus.

Oh, why not to-night? Oh, why not to-night?
Oh, why not to-night? why not to-night? Why not to-night? why not to-night?

Wilt thou be saved? Then why not to-night?
Wilt thou be saved? wilt thou be saved? Then why not, oh, why not to - night?

Gloria Patri

Glory be to the Father, and to the Son, And to the Ho-ly Ghost;
As it was in the beginning, is now, and ev - er shall be, World with-out end. A-men.

138 **What A Friend**

H. BONAR.   C. C. CONVERSE.

1. What a Friend we have in Je - sus, All our sins and griefs to bear!
2. Have we tri - als and temp-ta-tions? Is there trouble a - ny-where?
3. Are we weak and heavy la - den, Cumbered with a load of care?

What a priv - i - lege to car - ry Ev - 'ry-thing to God in pray'r!
We should never be dis-cour-aged, Take it to the Lord in pray'r.
Precious Sav-ior, still our ref - uge, Take it to the Lord in pray'r.

FINE.

D. S.—All be - cause we do not car - ry Ev - 'ry - thing to God in pray'r.
Je-sus knows our ev - 'ry weakness, Take it to the Lord in pray'r.
In His arms He'll take and shield thee, Thou wilt find a sol-ace there.

D. S.

O what peace we of-ten for - feit, O what needless pain we bear,
Can we find a friend so faith - ful Who will all our sor-rows share?
Do thy friends despise, forsake thee? Take it to the Lord in prayer;

139 **Blest Be The Tie**

JOHN FAWCETT.   (Dennis. S. M.)   H. G. NAGELI.

1. Blest be the tie that binds Our hearts in Chris - tian love;
2. Be - fore our Fa - ther's throne We pour our ar - dent pray'r;
3. We share our mu - tual woes, Our mu - tual bur - dens bear,
4. When we a - sun - der part, It gives us in - ward pain;

The fel - low ship of kin - dred minds Is like to that a - bove.
Our fears, our hopes, our aims are one, Our com - forts and our cares.
And oft - en for each oth - er flows The sym - pa - thiz - ing tear.
But we shall still be joined in heart, And hope to meet a - gain.

140 God Be With You

J. E. Rankin

W. G. Tomer

1. God be with you till we meet a-gain, By His coun-sels guide, up-hold you,
2. God be with you till we meet a-gain, 'Neath His wings protecting hide you,
3. God be with you till we meet a-gain, Keep love's banner float-ing o'er you;

With His sheep se-cure-ly fold you; God be with you till we meet a-gain!
Dai - ly man-na still pro - vide you; God be with you till we meet a-gain!
Smite death's threat'ning wave before you; God be with you till we meet a-gain!

CHORUS.

Till we meet,.... till we meet, Till we meet at Je - sus' feet;
Till we meet, till we meet a-gain, till we meet;

Till we meet..... till we meet, God be with you till we meet a-gain!
Till we meet, till we meet again,

141 Whisper A Prayer

Unknown

Copyright, 1944, by John T. Benson, Jr..

Arr. by Mrs. Jas. Pate

1. Whis-per a prayer in the morn - ing, Whis-per a prayer at noon;
2. God answers prayer in the morn - ing, God an-swers prayer at noon;
3. Je - sus may come in the morn - ing, Je - sus may come at noon;

Whis-per a prayer in the eve - ning, To keep your heart in tune.
God an-swers prayer in the eve - ning, To keep your heart in tune.
Je - sus' may come in the eve - ning, So keep your heart in tune.

Face To Face

Mrs. Frank A. Breck

Grant Colfax Tullar

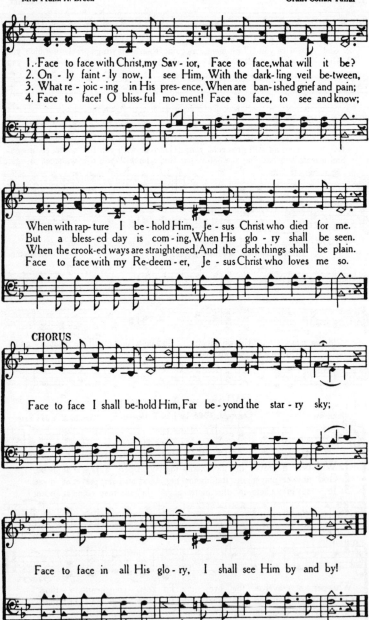

1. Face to face with Christ, my Sav - ior, Face to face, what will it be?
2. On - ly faint - ly now, I see Him, With the dark - ling veil be - tween,
3. What re - joic - ing in His pres - ence, When are ban - ished grief and pain;
4. Face to face! O bliss - ful mo - ment! Face to face, to see and know;

When with rap - ture I be - hold Him, Je - sus Christ who died for me.
But a bless - ed day is com - ing, When His glo - ry shall be seen.
When the crook-ed ways are straightened, And the dark things shall be plain.
Face to face with my Re - deem - er, Je - sus Christ who loves me so.

CHORUS

Face to face I shall be - hold Him, Far be - yond the star - ry sky;

Face to face in all His glo - ry, I shall see Him by and by!

143 Does Jesus Care

Frank E. Graeff   J. Lincoln Hall

1. Does Je-sus care when my heart is pained Too deep-ly for mirth or song,
2. Does Je-sus care when my way is dark With a nameless dread and fear?
3. Does Je-sus care when I've tried and failed To re-sist some temptation strong;
4. Does Je-sus care when I've said "goodby" To the dearest on earth to me,

As the burdens press, And the cares distress, And the way grows weary and long?
As the daylight fades Into deep night shades, Does He care enough to be near?
When for my deep grief There is no re-lief, Tho' my tears flow all the night long?
And my sad heart aches Till it nearly breaks, Is it aught to Him? does He see?

Chorus

O yes. He cares, I know He cares, His heart is touched with my grief;....

When the days are weary, The long night dreary, I know my Sav-ior cares.

He cares.

The Lily Of The Valley

"A friend loveth at all times." Pro. 17: 17.

English Melody.

1. I have found a friend in Je - sus, He's ev - 'ry - thing to me, He's the
2. He all my grief has ta - ken, and all my sor-rows borne; In temp-
3. He will nev - er, nev - er leave me, nor yet for - sake me here, While I

fair - est of ten thousand to my soul; The Lil - y of the Val-ley, in
ta-tion He's my strong and mighty tow'r; I have all for Him for-sa-ken, and
live by faith and do His bless-ed will; A wall of fire a-bout me, I've

D. S.—Lil - y of the val-ley, the

FINE

Him a - lone I see All I need to cleanse and make me ful - ly whole.
all my i - dols torn From my heart, and now He keeps me by His pow'r.
noth-ing now to fear, With His man - na He my hun - gry soul shall fill.

bright and Morn-ing Star, He's the fair - est of ten thou-sand to my soul.

In sor - row He's my com - fort, in troub - le He's my stay,
Tho' all the world for - sake me, and Sa - tan tempts me sore,
Then sweep-ing up to glo - ry, to see His bless - ed face,

D. S.

He tells me ev - 'ry care on Him to roll. He's the
Thro' Js - sus I shall safe - ly reach the goal, He's the
Where riv - ers of de - light shall ev - er roll, He's the

Hallelujah.

145 I Will Not Be A Stranger

J. B. S.   James B. Singleton

1. I will not be a stran-ger when I get to that cit-y, I'm ac-
2. I will not be a stran-ger when I get to that cit-y, I've a
3. I will not be a stran-ger when I get to that cit-y, There'll be

quaint-ed with folks o-ver there; There'll be friends there to greet me,
home on those streets paved with gold; I will feel right at home there
no lone-ly days o-ver there; There'll be no storm-y weath-er

S   **FINE**

there'll be loved ones to meet me, At the gates of that cit-y four-square.
in that beau-ti-ful "Somewhere," With my loved ones whose mem'ries I hold.
but a great get to-geth-er, On the streets of that cit-y four-square.

D. S.-get to that cit-y, I'm ac-quaint-ed with folks o-ver there.

CHORUS

Thru the years, thru the tears, they have gone one by one, But they'll wait at the

D. S.

gate, un-til my race is run; I will not be a stran-ger when I

Sweet By and By

S. Fillmore Bennett   by per.   Jos. P. Webster

1. There's a land that is fair-er than day, And by faith we can see it a-
2. We shall sing on that beau-ti-ful shore The me-lo-di-ous songs of the
3. To our boun-ti-ful Fa-ther a-bove, We will of-fer our trib-ute of

fai; For the Fa-ther waits o-ver the way, To pre-pare us a
blest, And our spir-its shall sor-row no more, Not a sigh for the
praise, For the glo-ri-ous gift of His love, And the bless-ings that

Chorus

dwell-ing place there. In the sweet   by and by,   We shall
bless-ing of rest.
hal-low our days.   In the sweet   by and by,

meet on that beau-ti-ful shore,   In the sweet   by and
by and by,   In the sweet

by,   We shall meet on that beau-ti-ful shore.
by and by,

147

In the Garden

C. A. M.   C. Austin Miles

1. I come to the gar-den a-lone,   While the dew is still on the
2. He speaks, and the sound of His voice   Is so sweet the birds hush their
3. I'd stay in the gar-den with Him   Though the night a-round me be

ros - es, And the voice I hear, Fall-ing on my ear, The
sing - ing, And the mel - o - dy That He gave to me, With-
fall - ing, But He bids me go; Thro' the voice of woe His

Son of God dis - clos - es.
in my heart is ring - ing.   **CHORUS** And He walks with me, and He
voice to me is call - ing.

talks with me, And He tells me I am His own; And the

joy we share as we tar-ry there, None oth-er has ev - er known.

Tell Mother I'll Be There

148

C. M. F.

Charles M. Fillmore

1. When I was but a lit-tle child how well I rec-ol-lect
2. Tho I was oft-en way-ward, she was al-ways kind and good;
3. When I be-came a prod-i-gal, and left the old roof-tree,
4. One day a mes-sage came to me, it bade me quick-ly come

How I would grieve my mother with my fol-ly and neg-lect; And
So pa-tient, gen-tle, lov-ing, when my ways were rough and rude; My
She al-most broke her lov-ing heart in mourn-ing aft-er me; And
If I would see my moth-er ere the Sav-ior took her home; I

now that she has gone to heav'n I miss her ten-der care: O Sav-ior, tell my
childhood griefs and trials she would gladly with me share: O Sav-ior, tell my
day and night she prayed to God to keep me in His care: O Sav-ior, tell my
promised her, be-fore she died, for heav-en to pre-pare: O Sav-ior, tell my

Rit.

Chorus

moth-er I'll be there!
I'll be there!

Tell mother I'll be there in answer to her pray'r;

This message, bless-ed Sav-ior, to her bear! Tell mother I'll be there, heav'n's

Tell Mother I'll Be There

Rit.

joys with her to share: Yes, tell my dar-ling mother I'll be there!

I'll be there!

149

At Calvary

Wm. R. Newell

D. B. Towner
Arranged John T. Benson, Jr.

1. Years I spent in van - i - ty and pride, Caring not my Lord was cru-ci-
2. By God's word at last my sin I learned; Then I trembled at the law I'd
3. Oh, the love that drew sal-va-tion's plan! Oh, the grace that bro't it down to

fied, Know-ing not it was for me He died On Cal - va - ry.
spurned, Till my guilt-y soul im-plor-ing turned To Cal - va - ry.
man! Oh, the might-y gulf that God did span At Cal - va - ry!

CHORUS

Mer-cy there was great, and grace was free; Pardon there was multiplied to me;

There my bur-dened soul found lib - er - ty. At Cal - va - ry.

Gathering Flowers for the Master's Bouquet

M. E. B.   Marvin E. Baumgardner

1. Death is an an-gel sent down from a-bove, Sent for the buds and the flow-ers we love; Tru-ly 'tis so, for in heav-en's own way Each soul is a flow'r in the Mas-ter's bouquet.

2. Loved ones are passing each day and each hour, Pass-ing a-way "as the life of a flow'r;" But ev-'ry bud and each blos-som some day Will bloom as a flow'r in the Mas-ter's bouquet.

3. Let us be faith-ful till life's work is done, Bloom-ing with love till the reap-er shall come; Then we'll be gath-ered to-geth-er for aye, Trans-plant-ed to bloom in the Mas-ter's bouquet.

Chorus

Gath-er-ing flow'rs for the Mas-ter's bouquet, Beau-ti-ful flow'rs that will nev-er de-cay; Gath-ered by an-gels and carried a-way For-ev-er to bloom in the Master's bouquet.

151 When I See The Blood

By Foote Bros., not copyrighted. Let no one do so. May this song ever be free to be published for the glory of God.

John J. G. F.

1. Christ our Re - deem - er died on the cross, Died for the sin - ner,
2. Chief - est of sin - ners, Je - sus can save, As He has prom-ised,
3. Judg - ment is com - ing, all will be there, Who have re - ject - ed,
4. O what com - pas - sion, oh bound - less love! Je - sus hath pow - er,

paid all His due; All who re - ceive Him need nev - er fear.
so will He do; Oh, sin - ner, hear Him, trust in His word,
who have re - fused? Oh, sin - ner, has - ten, let Je - sus in,
Je - sus is true; All who be - lieve are safe from the storm,

CHORUS

Yes, He will pass, will pass o - ver you. When I see the
Then He will pass, will pass o - ver you.
Then God will pass, will pass o - ver you.
Oh, He will pass, will pass o - ver you. When I

blood, When I see the blood, When I see the
see the blood, When I see the blood, When I

Rit

blood, I will pass, I will pass o - ver you.
see the blood, o - ver you.

Hark, the Herald Angels Sing

Charles Wesley   Mendelssohn

1. Hark! the her-ald an-gels sing, "Glo-ry to the new-born King;
2. Christ, by high-est heav'n a-dored, Christ, the ev-er-last-ing Lord:
3. Hail the heav'n-born Prince of Peace! Hail the Sun of right-eous-ness!
4. Come, De-sire of na-tions, come! Fix in us Thy hum-ble home:

Peace on earth, and mer-cy mild; God and sin-ners rec-on-ciled."
Late in time be-hold Him come, Off-spring of a vir-gin's womb.
Light and life to all He brings, Ris'n with heal-ing in His wings:
Rise, the wom-an's con-qu'ring seed, Bruise in us the ser-pent's head;

Joy-ful, all ye na-tions, rise, Join the tri-umph of the skies;
Veiled in flesh the God-head see, Hail th'in-car-nate De-i-ty!
Mild He lays His glo-ry by, Born that man no more may die;
Ad-am's like-ness now ef-face, Stamp Thine im-age in its place:

With an-gel-ic hosts pro-claim, "Christ is born in Beth-le-hem."
Pleased as man with men to ap-pear, Je-sus our Im-man-uel here.
Born to raise the sons of earth; Born to give them sec-ond birth.
Sec-ond Ad-am from a-bove, Re-in-state us in Thy love.

Hark! the Herald Angels Sing

Hark! the her - ald an - gels sing, "Glo - ry to the new - born King."

153 ## O Come, All Ye Faithful

Tr. by Frederick Oakeley

Wade's Cantus Diversi

1. O come, all ye faith - ful, joy - ful and tri - um - phant, O
2. Sing, choirs of an - gels, sing in ex - ul - ta - tion, O
3. Yea, Lord, we greet Thee, born this hap - py morn - ing,

come ye, O come ye to Beth - le - hem; Come and be - hold Him
sing, all ye bright hosts of heav'n a - bove; Glo - ry to God, all
Je - sus, to Thee be all glo - ry giv'n; Word of the Fa - ther,

CHORUS

born the King of an - gels.
glo - ry in the high - est. O come, let us a - dore Him, O come, let us a -
now in flesh ap - pear - ing.

dore Him, O come, let us a - dore Him, Christ, the Lord.

154 Silent Night, Holy Night

Joseph Mohr

Franz Gruber

1 { Si-lent night! } All is calm, all is bright; { Round yon virgin mother and Child, }
  { Ho-ly night! }   { Ho-ly Infant so tender and mild, }

2 { Si-lent night! } Shepherds quake at the sight; { Glories stream from heav-en a-far, }
  { Ho-ly night! }   { Heav'nly hosts sing Al-le-lu-ia, }

3 { Si-lent night! } Son of God, love's pure light; { Radiant beams from Thy holy face }
  { Ho-ly night! }   { With the dawn of redeeming grace, }

Sleep in heav-en-ly peace, Sleep in heav-en-ly peace.
Christ, the Sav-ior, is born! Christ the Sav-ior is born!
Je-sus, Lord, at Thy birth, Je-sus, Lord, at Thy birth.

155 Away in A Manger

M. L.

Martin Luther

1. A-way in a man-ger, No crib for a bed, The lit-tle Lord
2. The cat-tle are low-ing, The Ba-by a-wakes, But lit-tle Lord
3. Be near me, Lord Je-sus, I ask Thee to stay Close by me for-

Je-sus Laid down His sweet head; The stars in the sky Looked
Je-sus, No cry-ing He makes; I love Thee, Lord Je-sus! Look
ev-er, And love me, I pray; Bless all the dear chil-dren In

Away in A Manger

down where He lay,—The lit-tle Lord Je-sus, A-sleep on the hay.
down from the sky, And stay by my cra-dle, Till morn-ing is nigh.
Thy ten-der care, And take us to heav-en, To live with Thee there.

156

Joy To The World

Isaac Watts

Geo. F. Handel

1. Joy to the world! the Lord is come; Let earth re-ceive her King; Let
2. Joy to the world! the Sav-ior reigns; Let men their songs employ; While
3. He rules the world with truth and grace, And makes the na-tions prove The

ev-'ry heart pre-pare Him room, And heav'n and na-ture sing,
fields and floods rocks, hills, and plains Re-peat the sound-ing joy,
glo-ries of His right-eous-ness, And won-ders of His love,
And heav'n, and heav'n and na-

and heav'n and na-ture sing, And heav'n, and heav'n and na-ture sing.
re-peat the sound-ing joy, Re-peat, re-peat the sound-ing joy.
and won-ders of His love, And wonders, and won-ders of His love.
ture sing................

sing, And heav'n and nature sing,

157 Beautiful Star Of Bethlehem

Adger M. Pace   Theme by R. F. B.   R. Fisher Boyce.   Har. by A. M. P.

1. Oh, beau-ti-ful Star of Beth-le-hem, shin-ing a-far thru shadows dim,
2. Oh, beau-ti-ful Star the hope of light, guid-ing the pil-grim thru the night,
3. Oh, beau-ti-ful Star, the hope of rest, for the redeemed, the good and blest,

Giv-ing a light for those who long have gone, have gone; And guiding the wise men
O-ver the mountain till the break of dawn, the dawn; And in-to the light of
Yon-der in glo-ry when the crown is won, is won; For Je-sus is now that

D. S.-Oh, give us thy light to

on their way un-to the place where Jesus lay,
per-fect day it will give out a love-ly ray, Beauti-ful Star of Beth-le-
Star di-vine, brighter and brighter He will shine.

light the way in-to the land of per-fect day,

FINE   CHORUS

hem shine on.   Oh, beau-ti-ful Star   of
      shine on.   Beau-ti-ful, beau-ti-ful Star,

D. S.

Beth-le-hem,   Shine up-on us un-til the glo-ry dawn;
   Star of Beth-le-hem,   glo-ry dawn;

O Happy Day

Philip Doddridge.

E. F. Rimbault.

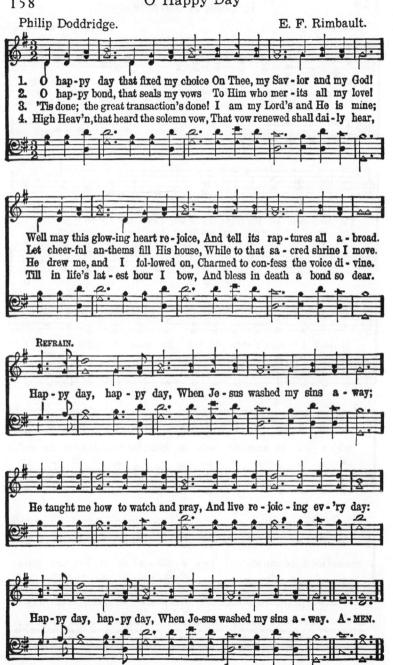

1. O hap-py day that fixed my choice On Thee, my Sav-ior and my God!
2. O hap-py bond, that seals my vows To Him who mer-its all my love!
3. 'Tis done; the great transaction's done! I am my Lord's and He is mine;
4. High Heav'n, that heard the solemn vow, That vow renewed shall dai-ly hear,

Well may this glow-ing heart re-joice, And tell its rap-tures all a-broad.
Let cheer-ful an-thems fill His house, While to that sa-cred shrine I move.
He drew me, and I fol-lowed on, Charmed to con-fess the voice di-vine.
Till in life's lat-est hour I bow, And bless in death a bond so dear.

REFRAIN.

Hap-py day, hap-py day, When Je-sus washed my sins a-way;

He taught me how to watch and pray, And live re-joic-ing ev-'ry day:

Hap-py day, hap-py day, When Je-sus washed my sins a-way. A-MEN.

It Took A Miracle

J. W. P.

John W. Peterson

1. My Father is om-ni-po-tent, And that you can't de-ny,
2. Though here His glo-ry has been shown; We still can't full-y see
3. The Bi-ble tells us of His pow'r And wis-dom all way through;

A God of might and mir-a-cles 'Tis writ-ten in the sky.
The won-ders of His might, His throne; 'Twill take e-ter-ni-ty.
And ev-'ry lit-tle bird and flow'r Are tes-ti-mo-nies, too.

CHORUS

It took a mir-a-cle to put the stars in place. It took a
mir-a-cle to hang the world in space. But when He saved my soul,
cleansed and made me whole, It took a mir-a-cle of love and grace.

160 In The Shelter Of His Arms

Words and Music by
Ike Davis & Ray Heady

1. When my soul was disturbed with sorrow, When my heart was burdened with sin; Jesus opened His arms of mercy and tenderly took me in.

2. There are storms that we all encounter, Do not fear they will do you no harm; In the Lord you will find protection, In the shelter of His arms.

3. Tho the world all around be raging, And it's filled with many alarms; Trust in Jesus and He will keep you, In the shelter of His arms.

CHORUS

There is peace in the time of trouble There is peace in the midst of the storm, There is peace tho the world be raging, In the shelter of His arms.

I Know Who Holds Tomorrow
(But I Know Who Holds my Hand)

Words and Music by Ira Stanphill

1. I don't know a-bout to-mor-row, I just live from day to
2. Ev-'ry step is get-ting bright-er as the gold-en stairs I
3. I don't know a-bout to-mor-row, It may bring me pov-er-

day; I don't bor-row from its sun-shine, For its skies may
climb; Ev-'ry bur-den's get-ting light-er, Ev-'ry cloud is
ty; But the one who feeds the spar-row, Is the one who

turn to gray; I don't wor-ry o'er the fu-ture, For I
sil-ver lined; There the sun is al-ways shin-ing, There no
stands by me; And the path that be my por-tion, May be

know what Je-sus said, And to-day I'll walk be-side Him,
tear will dim the eye; At the end-ing of the rain-bow,
thru the flame or flood, But His pres-ence goes be-fore me,

CHORUS

For He knows what is a-head.
Where the moun-tains touch the sky. Man-y things a-bout to-
And I'm cov-ered with His blood.

I Know Who Holds Tomorrow

mor-row I don't seem to un-der-stand; But I know who holds to-mor-row, And I know who holds my hand.

162 Near the Cross

Fanny J. Crosby

W. H. Doane

1. Je-sus, keep me near the cross, There a pre-cious fountain, Free to all, a
2. Near the cross, a trembling soul, Love and mer-cy found me; There the Bright and
3. Near the cross! O Lamb of God, Bring its scenes be-fore me; Help me walk from
4. Near the cross I'll watch and wait, Hop-ing, trust-ing, ev - er, Till I reach the

CHORUS

heal - ing stream, Flows from Cal-v'ry's mountain.
Morn-ing Star Shed His beams a-round me.   In the cross, in the cross,
day to day, With its shad-ows o'er me.
gold-en strand, Just be-yond the riv - er.

Be my glo-ry ev - er, Till my raptured soul shall find Rest be-yond the riv - er.

He'll Understand And Say "Well Done"

Words and Melody by LUCY E. CAMPBELL   ARR. for JOHN T. BENSON, JR.

1. If when you give the best of your serv-ice, Tell-ing the world that the Sav-iour is come; Be not dis-mayed when men don't be-lieve you, He un-der-stands; He'll say, "Well done."

2. Mis-un-der-stood, the Sav-iour of sin-ners, Hung on the cross; He was God's on-ly Son; Oh! hear Him call His Fa-ther in heav-en, "Let not my will, but Thine be done."

3. If when this life of la-bor is end-ed, And the re-ward of the race you have run; Oh! take the sweet rest pre-pared for faith-ful, Will be His blest, and fi-nal, "Well done."

4. But if you try and fail in your try-ing, Hands sore and scarred from the work you've be-gun; Take up your cross, run quick-ly to meet Him, He'll un-der-stand, He'll say, "Well done."

CHORUS

Oh, when I come to the end of my jour-ney, Wea-ry of life and the bat-tle is won; Car-'ing the staff and the

He'll Understand And Say "Well Done"

cross of re-demp-tion, He'll un-der-stand and say "Well done."

164   In Times Like These

Mrs. R. C. J.   Copyright, 1944, by Ruth Caye Jones   Mrs. Ruth Caye Jones

1. In times like these you need a Sav-iour, In times like these you need an
2. In times like these you need the Bi-ble, In times like these, oh, be not
3. In times like these I have a Sav-iour, In times like these, I have an

an-chor; Be ver-y sure, be ver-y sure, Be ver-y sure, be ver-y sure,
i-dle; Be ver-y sure, be ver-y sure, Be ver-y sure, be ver-y sure,
an-chor; I'm ver-y sure, I'm ver-y sure, I'm ver-y sure, I'm ver-y sure,

FINE   CHORUS

Your an-chor holds and grips the Sol-id Rock! This Rock is
Your an-chor holds
My an-chor holds

D.S.

Je-sus, Yes, He's the One, This Rock is Je-sus, The on-ly One.

I'll Fly Away

A. E. B.   Albert E. Brumley

1. Some glad morn-ing when this life is o'er, I'll fly a-
2. When the shad-ows of this life have grown,
3. Just a few more wea-ry days and then, fly a-way

way; To a home on God's ce-les-tial shore,
Like a bird from pris-on bars has flown,
fly a-way; To a land where joys shall nev-er end,

CHORUS

I'll fly a-way. I'll fly a-
fly a-way fly a-way. fly a-way

way, O glo-ry, I'll fly a-way; When I die,
fly a-way, in the morn-ing,

Hal-le-lu-jah, by and by, I'll fly a-way.
fly a-way fly a-way.

Mansions Over The Hilltop

Ira Stanphill

I. S.

1. I'm sat-is-fied with just a cot-tage be-low, A lit-tle sil-ver
2. Tho' of-ten tempt-ed tor - ment-ed and test-ed And like the proph-et
3. Don't think me poor or de - sert-ed or lone-ly, I'm not dis-couraged,

and a lit - tle gold; But in that cit - y where the ransomed will shine,
my pil-low a stone; And tho' I find here no per-manent dwelling,
I'm heav - en bound; I'm just a pil-grim in search of a cit - y,

CHORUS

I want a gold one that's sil - ver lined.
I know He'll give me a man-sion my own.
I want a man-sion, a harp and a crown.

I've got a mansion just

o - ver the hill - top, In that bright land where we'll never grow old, And some day

yonder we will nev - er-more wander But walk the streets that are purest gold.

167 When My Savior Reached Down For Me

G. E. W.   G. E. Wright

1. Once my soul was a-stray from the heav-en-ly way, And was wretch-ed and
2. I was near to de-spair when He came to me there, And He showed me that
3. How my heart does rejoice when I hear His sweet voice In the temp-est, to

vile as could be; But my Sav-ior in love gave me peace from a-bove,
I could be free; Then He lift-ed my feet, gave me gladness complete,
Him I then flee, There to lean on His arm, safe, se-cure from all harm,

Chorus

1-2 When He reached down His hand for me.   When my Savior reached down for
3 Since He   for me.

me,   When my Sav-ior reached down for me;   I was lost and un-
for me,   for me;

done, without God or His Son, When my Sav-ior reached down for me.
                                                    for me.

Wings Of A Dove

B. F.

Bob Ferguson

1. When troubles surround us, When e-vils come, The bod-y grows
2. When No-ah had drift-ed On the flood man-y days, He searched for
3. When Je-sus went down To the wa-ters that day, He was bap-

weak, The spir-it grows numb; When these things be-set us,
land, In var-i-ous ways; Trou-bles he had some,
tized, In the us-u-al way; When it was done,

He doesn't for-get us, He sends down His love On the wings of a dove.
But wasn't for-got-ten, He sent him His love On the wings of a dove.
God blessed His Son, He sent Him His love On the wings of a dove.

CHORUS

On the wings of a snow white dove He sends His pure sweet love, A sign from a-bove On the wings of a dove.

I'm Bound For The Kingdom

M. L.   Mosie Lister

1. You may ask me where I'm head-ed, you may ask me where I'm bound,
2. Well, I'm go-ing to a coun-try where they say we'll nev-er die,

Well, I'm go-ing to a coun-try 'cross the sea; And I know I'll
'Twill be end-less joy and glo-ry there for me; Yes, I know I'll

have a man-sion, and I know I'll have a crown, Well I'm bound for the
live for-ev-er in that cit-y in the sky,

king-dom of the free. Yes, I'm bound For the king-dom

CHORUS

of the bless-ed and the free, And my Je-sus soon is com-ing aft-er

I'm Bound For The Kingdom

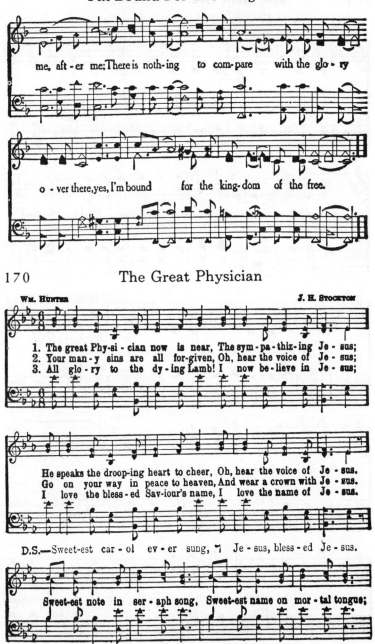

me, aft-er me; There is noth-ing to com-pare with the glo-ry

o - ver there, yes, I'm bound for the king-dom of the free.

170   The Great Physician

WM. HUNTER   J. H. STOCKTON

1. The great Phy-si - cian now is near, The sym - pa - thiz-ing Je - sus;
2. Your man - y sins are all for-given, Oh, hear the voice of Je - sus;
3. All glo - ry to the dy - ing Lamb! I now be - lieve in Je - sus;

He speaks the droop-ing heart to cheer, Oh, hear the voice of Je - sus.
Go on your way in peace to heaven, And wear a crown with Je - sus.
I love the bless - ed Sav-iour's name, I love the name of Je - sus.

D.S.—Sweet-est car - ol ev - er sung, ᴎ Je - sus, bless - ed Je - sus.

Sweet-est note in ser - aph song, Sweet-est name on mor - tal tongue;

171 Love Held Him To The Cross

C. W. Brown

1. All a - lone on the cross Je - sus suf - fered, Son of God though re-
2. All the good He had done was for - got - ten, Those He helped, healed and

ject - ed of men; Yet He prayed "Thine be done, God for - give them"
blessed fled in fear; "Cru - ci - fy, Cru - ci - fy Him" cried the sin - ner,

CHORUS

It was love that held the Lord up - on the cross. It was love
It was love

that held the Lord up - on the cross, Matchless love
Match - less love

For all the world He paid the cost; But the nails thru His hands could not

Love Held Him To The Cross

hold Him. It was love that held the Lord up-on the cross.

172 Higher Ground

Johnson Oatman, Jr.

Chas. H. Gabriel
Arranged by John T. Benson, Jr.

1. I'm press-ing on the up-ward way. New heights I'm gain-ing ev-'ry
2. My heart has no de-sire to stay Where doubts a-rise and fears dis-
3. I want to scale the ut-most height, And catch a gleam of glo-ry

day; Still pray-ing as I'm onward bound, "Lord, plant my feet on higher ground."
may; Tho' some may dwell where these abound, My prayer, my aim, is high-er ground.
bright; But still I'll pray till heav'n I've found, "Lord, lead me on to higher ground."

CHORUS

Lord, lift me up and let me stand, By faith, on heav-en's ta-ble

land, A high-er plane than I have found; Lord, plant my feet on high-er ground.

SPIRITUAL

Cleavant Derricks

1. I once was lost in sin but Je-sus took me in, And then a lit-tle
2. Some-times my path seems drear, with-out a ray of cheer, And then a cloud of
3. I may have doubts and fears, my eyes be filled with tears, But Je-sus is a

light from heav-en filled my soul; It bathed my heart in love and wrote my
doubt may hide the light of day; The mists of sin may rise and hide the
Friend Who watches day and night; I go to Him in prayer, He knows my

name a-bove, And just a lit-tle talk with Je-sus made me whole.
star-ry skies, But just a lit-tle talk with Je-sus clears the way.
ev-'ry care, And just a lit-tle talk with Je-sus makes it right.

CHORUS

Have a lit-tle talk with Je-sus, tell Him all a-bout our
Now let us   let us

trou-bles, Hear our faint-est cry an-swer by and by;
He will   and He will

Just A Little Talk With Jesus

Feel a lit-tle prayer wheel turn-ing   know a lit-tle fire is
Now when you   Then you'll

burn-ing,   Find a lit-tle talk with Je-sus makes it right.
You will   it makes it right.

174   Jesus Loves Me

Anna B. Warner   Wm. B. Bradbury

1. Je - sus loves me! this I know, For the Bi - ble tells me so; Lit - tle
2. Je - sus loves me! He who died, Heav-en's gates to o - pen wide; He will
3. Je - sus loves me! loves me still, Tho' I'm ver - y weak and ill; From His

CHORUS

ones to Him be - long, They are weak but He is strong.
wash a - way my sin, Let His lit - tle child come in. Yes, Je - sus loves me,
shin - ing throne on high, Comes to watch me where I lie.

Yes, Je - sus loves me. Yes, Je - sus loves me, The Bi - ble tells me so.

My God Is Real

K. M.

Kenneth Morris

1. There are some things ...... I may not know, ... There are some places I can't go, But I am sure .... of this one thing .... That God is real for I can feel Him deep within.

2. Some folk may doubt, ... some folk may scorn, ... All can go on and leave me a-lone, But as for me .... I'll take God's part, ... And God is real for I can feel Him in my heart.

3. I cannot tell .... just how you felt .... When Jesus took your sins a--way, But since that day .... yes, since that hour .... God has been real for I can feel His ho-ly pow'r.

CHORUS

My God is real, real in my

My God Is Real

soul, My God is real for He has washed and made me
real in my soul, Real washed

whole; His love for me is like pure gold,
made me whole; His love for me is like pure gold,

My God is real for I can feel Him in my soul.
Real feel ransomed soul.

176 Nearer, My God, To Thee

Sarah F. Adams

Lowell Mason

1. Near-er, my God to Thee, Nearer to Thee; E'en tho' it be a cross
2. Tho' like a wan-der-er, The sun goes down; Dark-ness be o-ver me,
3. There let the way ap-pear, Steps un-to heav'n; All that Thou send-est me,

D. S.—Near-er, my God, to Thee,

FINE

D.S.

That rais-eth me. Still all my song shall be, Near-er, my God, to Thee,
My rest a stone. Yet in my dreams I'd be, Near-er, my God, to Thee,
In mer-cy giv'n. An-gels to beck-on me Near-er, my God, to Thee,

Near-er to Thee.

Redeemed

JAMES ROWE

S. A. GANUS

1. Sweet is the song.......... I am sing-ing to - day;......
2. Great is my joy.......... now as on-ward I go; ......
3. Pre - cious in - deed.......... is my Sav - ior to me;......

.... I'm re - deemed!.... I'm re - deemed!.... Trou-ble and
.... I'm re - deemed!.... I'm re - deemed!.... All the way
.... I'm re - deemed!.... I'm re - deemed!.... Hap-py in

sor - row .... have van-ished a - way;..........
homeward .... my prais-es shall flow;..........
glo - ry.......... some day I shall be; ....

I have

Chorus

I have been redeemed! I'm re - deemed by love di - vine,
been re-deemed! I'm redeemed by love divine,

Glo-ry, glo-ry, Christ is mine, Christ is mine, All to him I
Christ is mine, All to him

Redeemed

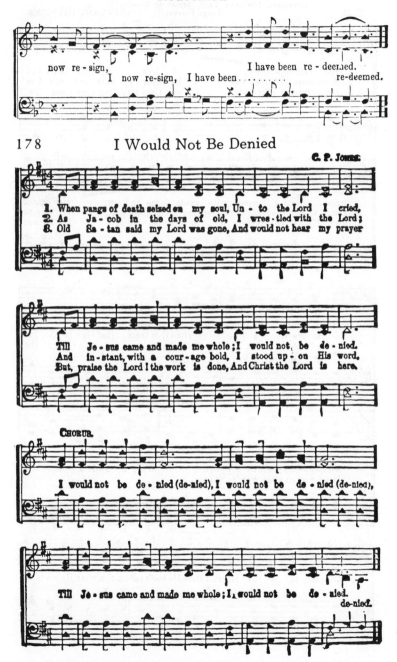

now re - sign, I have been re - deemed.

I now re-sign, I have been.......... re-deemed.

178 I Would Not Be Denied

C. P. JONES.

1. When pangs of death seized on my soul, Un - to the Lord I cried,
2. As Ja - cob in the days of old, I wres - tled with the Lord;
3. Old Sa - tan said my Lord was gone, And would not hear my prayer

Till Je - sus came and made me whole; I would not, be de - nied.
And in - stant, with a cour - age bold, I stood up - on His word,
But, praise the Lord! the work is done, And Christ the Lord is here.

CHORUS.

I would not be de - nied (de-nied), I would not be de - nied (de-nied),

Till Je - sus came and made me whole; I would not be de - nied.
de-nied.

179   When God Dips His Love In My Heart

C. D.   CLEAVANT DERRICKS

1. When God dips His pen of love in my heart And
2. Sometimes tho' the way is drear - y, dark and cold, And
3. He walked ev - 'ry step up Cal - v'ry's rug - ged way To

writes my soul a mes-sage He wants me to know, His Spir-it
some un-burdened sor - row keeps me from the goal, I go to
give His life com-plete-ly, and bring a bet - ter day; My life was

all di - vine fills this sin - ful soul of mine, When
God in prayer, I can al-ways find Him there (hal - le - lu-jah!) To
steeped in sin, but in love He took me in, His

REFRAIN

God dips His love in my heart.
whisper sweet peace to my soul. Well, I said I wouldn't
blood washed away ev - 'ry stain.

tell it to a liv - ing soul How He bro't sal-va-tion when He made me

When God Dips His Love In My Heart

whole, But I found I couldn't hide such love as Je-sus did im-part;

'Cause it makes me   Laugh and it makes me cry   then it sets my

sin-ful soul on fire, hal-le-lu-jah! When God dips His love in my heart.

180   Revive Us Again

Wm. P. Mackay   J. J. Husband

1. We praise Thee, O God, for the Son of Thy love, For Je-sus, Who died and is
2. All glo-ry and praise to the Lamb that was slain, Who has borne all our sins and has
3. Re-vive us a-gain, fill each heart with Thy love, May each soul be rekindled with

CHORUS

now gone above.
cleansed ev'ry stain. Hal-le-lu-jah! Thine the glory, Hallelujah! amen; Re-vive us a-gain.
fire from a-bove.

181 Nothing Can Compare

M. L.
Mosie Lister

1. For years I've trav-eled this wide world o-ver, And I've seen
2. Tho' just a beg-gar, I have no man-sion, No gold and
3. If I could choose now be-tween the whole world And the small-est

beau - ties, So rich and rare; But where I'm go - ing
sil - ver, No jew - els rare; But in the morn - ing
man - sion In heav - en fair; I'd choose to go there,

Is so much bet - ter, Down here there's noth-ing that can compare.
When I reach heav-en, I know I'll be a mill-ion-aire.
It's so much bet - ter, That all earth's glo - ry can-not com-pare.

CHORUS

Oh, there is noth - ing that can com - pare, With all the

Nothing Can Compare

beau - ty and glo - ry there; My Lord is build - ing a man - sion there. And there is noth - ing that can com -

Coda

pare, Oh, there is noth - ing that can com - pare.

182   Jesus, Lover Of My Soul

Charles Wesley   S. B. Marsh

1 Je - sus, lov - er of my soul, Let me to Thy bos - om fly,   Hide me, O my
    While the near-er wa - ters roll, While the tempest still is high;   Till the storm of

2 Oth - er ref - uge have I none, Hangs my helpless soul on Thee;   All my trust on
    Leave, O leave me not a - lone, Still support and comfort me.   All my help from

3 Plenteous grace with Thee is found, Grace to cover all my sin.   Thou of life the
    Let the healing streams abound, Make and keep me pure within.   Free - ly let me

Sav - ior hide,   Safe in - to the ha - ven guide, O re-ceive my soul at last.
life is past;

Thee is stayed,   Cov - er my defenceless head With the shadow of Thy wing.
Thee I bring,

Foun - tain art,   Spring Thou up within my heart, Rise to all e - ter - ni - ty.
take of Thee,

Whispering Hope

Alice Hawthorne International Copyright Secured Arranged by John T. Benson, Jr.

1. Soft as the voice of an an-gel, Breathing a les-son un-heard,
2. If in the dusk of the twi-light, Dim be the re-gion a-far,
3. Hope, as an an-chor so stead-fast, Rends the dark veil for the soul,

Hope with a gen-tle per-sua-sion Whis-pers her com-fort-ing word:
Will not the deep-en-ing dark-ness Bright-en the glim-mer-ing star?
Whith-er the Mas-ter has en-tered, Rob-bing the grave of its goal;

Wait till the dark-ness is o-ver, Wait till the tem-pest is done,
Then when the night is up-on us, Why should the heart sink a-way?
Come then, O come, glad fru-i-tion. Come to my sad, wea-ry heart;

Hope for the sun-shine to-mor-row, Aft-er the show-er is
When the dark mid-night is o-ver, Watch for the break-ing of
Come, O Thou blest hope of glo-ry, Nev-er, O nev-er de-

CHORUS

gone. Whis - - - - per-ing hope, O how
day.
part. Whis-per-ing hope, Whis-per-ing hope,

Whispering Hope

Wel - - - come thy voice, Mak - - - ing my
Wel-come thy voice, O how wel-come thy voice, Mak-ing my heart,

heart in its sor - - - row re-joice.
mak-ing my heart, in its sor-row, its sor-rows re-joice.

184

My Jesus, I Love Thee

Anonymous

GORDON

A. J. Gordon

1 My Je - sus, I love Thee, I know Thou art mine, For Thee all the
2. I love Thee, be-cause Thou hast first lov-ed me, And purchased my
3. I'll love Thee in life, I will love Thee in death, And praise Thee as
4. In man-sions of glo-ry and end-less de-light, I'll ev-er a-

fol - lies of sin I re-sign; My gra-cious Re-deem - er, my Sav-
par - don on Cal-va-ry's tree; I love Thee for wear - ing the thorns
long as Thou lend-est me breath; And say when the death - dew lies cold
dore Thee in heav-en so bright; I'll sing with the glit - ter-ing crown

ior art Thou; If ev - er I loved Thee, my Je - sus, 'tis now.
on Thy brow; If ev - er I loved Thee, my Je - sus, 'tis now.
on my brow; If ev - er I loved Thee, my Je - sus, 'tis now.
on my brow; If ev - er I loved Thee, my Je - sus, 'tis now.

185

There's Coming A Day

W. E. M.   W. Elmo Mercer

1. There's coming a day in God's tomorrow, When trials are past and hea-
2. The dawning will come and I'll see Je-sus Just waiting for me on hea-

ven's in view. No burdens to bear, no tears of sorrow, For God will be
ven's bright shore. I'll rush to His side and say, "Dear Master, I'm coming back

near to car-ry me through. The gates will o-pen and I shall enter
home to wander no more." O bliss-ful moment on yonder portals,

My home for-ev-er with Him to stay. What glo-ry 'twill be when I see
I'll praise my Je-sus, the Truth, the Way. Till then I will be a happy

Je-sus, My won-der-ful Lord, There's com-ing a day.
pil-grim, My jour-ney will end, There's com-ing a day.

We're Marching To Zion

Isaac Watts   Robert Lowry

1. Come, we that love the Lord, And let our joys be known, Join
2. Let those re-fuse to sing Who nev-er knew our God; But
3. The hill of Zi-on yields A thou-sand sa-cred sweets, Be-
4. Then let our songs a-bound, And ev-'ry tear be dry; We're

in a song with sweet ac-cord, Join in a song with sweet ac-cord,
chil-dren of the heav-'nly King, But chil-dren of the heav'n-ly King,
fore we reach the heav-'nly fields, Be-fore we reach the heav'n-ly fields,
marching thru Im-man-uel's ground, We're marching thru Im-manuel's ground,

And thus sur - round the throne, And thus sur-round the throne.
May speak their joys a-broad, May speak their joys a-broad.
Or walk the gold-en streets, Or walk the gold-en streets.
To fair - er worlds on high, To fair-er worlds on high.

(1) And thus sur-round the throne, And thus sur-round the throne.

Chorus

We're march - ing to Zi-on, beau-ti-ful, beau-ti-ful Zi-on; We're
We're march-ing on to Zi-on,

march-ing up-ward to Zi-on, The beau-ti-ful ci-ty of God.
Zi-on, Zi-on,

What A Savior

M. P. D.   in "Guiding Hand"   Marvin P. Dalton

Legato

1. Once I was stray-ing in sin's dark val-ley, No hope with-in could I
2. He left the Fa-ther, with all His rich-es, With calm-ness sweet and se-
3. Death's chill-y wa-ters I'll soon be cross-ing, His hand will lead me safe

see; They searched thru heav-en and found a Sav-ior To save a
rene, Came down from heav-en and gave His life-blood, To make the
o'er; I'll join the cho-rus in that great cit-y, And sing up

CHORUS

poor lost soul like me.
vil-est sin-ner clean.   O what a Sav-ior, O hal-le-
there for-ev-er-more.

lu-jah, His heart was bro-ken on Cal-va-ry; His hands were

rit.

nail-scarred, His side was riv-en, He gave His life-blood for e-ven me.

At An Altar Of Prayer

Words & Music by
Ike Davis and Ray E. Heady

1. Man-y long years a-go from heav-en, Came a man of
2. Man-y times when my heart is heav-y, I need some-one that
3. If your heart is weighed down with problems And you're caught in

beau-ty so rare With a heart full of love and mer-cy He
I know who cares; And the one that I need is Je-sus, I
sin's wick-ed snare; You will find peace and rest in the Sav-ior, Just

met me at an al-tar of prayer.
find Him at an al-tar of prayer. At an al-tar of prayer I met
meet Him at an al-tar of prayer.

Je-sus, With compas-sion He welcomed me there; And my bur-den so

heav-y was lift-ed, When we met at an al-tar of prayer.

Dwelling in Beulah Land

C. A. M.

C. Austin Miles

1. Far a-way the noise of strife up-on my ear is fall-ing, Then I know the
2. Far be-low the storm of doubt up-on the world is beat-ing, Sons of men in
3. Let the stormy breez-es blow, their cry can not a-larm me, I am safe-ly
4. View-ing here the works of God, I sink in con-tem-pla-tion, Hear-ing now His

sins of earth be-set on ev-'ry hand; Doubt and fear and things of earth in
bat-tle long the en-e-my with-stand; Safe am I with-in the cas-tle
sheltered here, pro-tect-ed by God's hand; Here the sun is al-ways shin-ing,
bless-ed voice, I see the way He planned; Dwell-ing in the Spir-it, here I

vain to me are call-ing, None of these shall move me from Beu-lah Land.
of God's word re-treat-ing, Noth-ing there can reach me—'tis Beu-lah Land.
here there's naught can harm me, I am safe for-ev-er in Beu-lah Land.
learn of full sal-va-tion, Glad-ly will I tar-ry in Beu-lah Land.

CHORUS

I'm liv-ing on the moun-tain, un-der-neath a cloud-less sky, I'm
Praise God!

drink-ing at the foun-tain that nev-er shall run dry, O yes! I'm feasting on the

Dwelling in Beulah Land

man-na from a boun-ti-ful sup-ply, For I am dwelling in Beu-lah Land.

190   Look And Live

W. A. O.

W. A. Ogden.

1. I've a message from the Lord, Hal-le-lu-jah! The message un-to you I'll give;
2. I've a message full of love, Hal-le-lu-jah! A message, O my friend, for you;
3. Life is of-fered un-to you, Hal-le-lu-jah! E - ter-nal life thy soul shall have,
4. I will tell you how I came, Hal-le-lu-jah! To Jesus when He made me whole:

FINE.

'T is re-cord-ed in His word, Hal-le-lu-jah! It is on-ly that you "look and live."
'T is a message from above, Hal-le-lu-jah! Je-sus said it, and I know 'tis true.
If you'll on-ly look to Him, Hal-le-lu-jah! Look to Jesus, who a-lone can save.
'T was believing on His name, Hal-le-lu-jah! I trusted, and He saved my soul.

D.S.—'T is recorded in His word, Hal-le-lu-jah! It is on-ly that you "look and live."

CHORUS.

D. S.

"Look and live," ......my brother, live,   Look to Je-sus now and live;
    "Look and live," my brother, live, "Look and live,"

191 There's A Difference

W. E. M.   W. Elmo Mercer

1. Some peo - ple go to church 'most ev - 'ry Sun - day morn; For
2. The Sav - ior said one day, not ev - 'ry one who speaks The

they be - lieve there is a God a - bove; God a - bove; They
name of God shall en - ter heav - en's gate heav - en's gate; You

live the Gold - en Rule; Their Bi - bles, too, are worn; Their
must be made a - new, Sal - va - tion you must seek; Have

CHORUS

hearts are filled with bro - ther-hood and love and love. But there's a diff -
faith in Him be - fore it is too late too late. For

rence,   There's a diff'rence,   You can have re - lig - ion,
There's a diff'rence   There's a diff'rence

There's A Difference

go to church, and pray, and still be lost in sin; There's a diff'rence
lost in sin; There's

There's a diff'rence If you want to see heaven,
a diff'rence; There's a diff'rence;

if you want real joy then you must be born a-gain.
born a-gain.

192 The Old-Time Religion

Arranged.

Cho. —'Tis the old time re-lig-ion, 'Tis the old time re-lig-ion,
1. It was good for our moth-ers, It was good for our moth-ers,

'Tis the old time re-lig-ion,—It's good e-nough for me.
It was good for our moth-ers,—It's good e-nough for me.

2 Makes me love everybody. 6 It was tried in the fiery furnace.
3 It has sav-ed our fathers. 7 It was good for Paul and Silas.
4 It was good for the Prophet Daniel. 8 It will do when I am dying.
5 It was good for the Hebrew children. 9 It can take us all to heaven.

How About Your Heart

B. S. T.

Bennie S. Triplett

1. How a - bout your heart? Is it right with God? That's the thing that
2. Friend, how would you feel? If your heart were made, With a win-dow

counts to - day; Is it black by sin? Is it pure with-in?
on each side; So that all could see, Not just outward charm,

CHORUS

Could you ask Christ in to stay? Peo-ple of-ten
But de - tect if in -ward harm? Ooh - ah - - ooh,

see you As you are out - side, Je - sus
Ooh - ah - - ooh,

real - ly knows you, For He sees in -side; How a-bout your

How About Your Heart

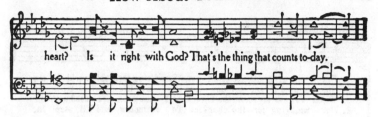

heart? Is it right with God? That's the thing that counts to-day.

194   Sweet Hour Of Prayer

W. W. Walford

Wm. B. Bradbury

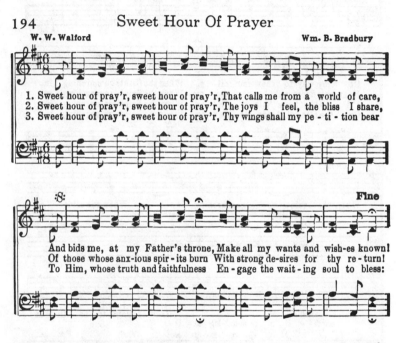

1. Sweet hour of pray'r, sweet hour of pray'r, That calls me from a world of care,
2. Sweet hour of pray'r, sweet hour of pray'r, The joys I feel, the bliss I share,
3. Sweet hour of pray'r, sweet hour of pray'r, Thy wings shall my pe - ti - tion bear

Fine

And bids me, at my Father's throne, Make all my wants and wish-es known!
Of those whose anx-ious spir - its burn With strong de-sires for thy re-turn!
To Him, whose truth and faithfulness En - gage the wait-ing soul to bless:

D. S.—And oft es-capes the tempter's snare By the re-turn, sweet hour of pray'r.
D. S.—And glad-ly take my sta - tion there, And wait for thee, sweet hour of pray'r.
D. S.—I'll cast on Him my ev - 'ry care, And wait for thee, sweet hour of pray'r.

D. S.

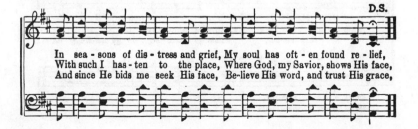

In sea - sons of dis - tress and grief, My soul has oft - en found re - lief,
With such I has - ten to the place, Where God, my Savior, shows His face,
And since He bids me seek His face, Be - lieve His word, and trust His grace,

195 When The Saints Go Marching In

Verses by JOHN T. BENSON JR.
Chorus Traditional

Arranged by H. F. HAMMOND

1. I'm a pil-grim and a stran-ger Wan-d'ring thro' this world of sin,
2. Oh, I know I'll see my Sav-iour If my life is free from sin,
3. When we gath-er 'round the Throne And the gates are closed with-in,
4. I'm wait-ing for the char-iot To swing low and I'll step in.

On my way to that fair cit-y, When the Saints go marching in.
Heav-en's doors will o-pen for me When the Saints go marching in.
I'll be shout-ing "Glo-ry, Glo-ry" When the Saints go marching in.
On the clouds I'll ride to Heav-en When the Saints go marching in;

CHORUS

When the saints go marching in, When the saints go
When the saints marching in, Saints go

march-ing in; Lord I want to be in that
march-ing in go march-ing in O

num-ber When the saints go march-ing in.
that num-ber, Saints go march-ing in go march-ing in.

count-less num-ber,

© 1956 in "Heart Warming Songs" by John T. Benson, Jr., owner

He Is Able To Deliver Thee

W. A. O.

WILLIAM A. OGDEN

1. 'Tis the grandest theme thro' the a - ges rung; 'Tis the grandest theme for a
2. 'Tis the grandest theme in the earth or main; 'Tis the grandest theme for a
3. 'Tis the grandest theme, let the ti - dings roll To the guilt-y heart, to the

mor - tal tongue; 'Tis the grand-est theme that the world e'er sung, "Our
mor - tal strain; 'Tis the grand-est theme, tell the world a - gain, "Our
sin - ful soul; Look to God in faith, He will make thee whole; "Our

CHORUS

God is a - ble to de - liv - er thee." He is a - - - ble to de-
a - ble, He is a - ble

liv - er thee, He is a - - - ble to de - liv - er thee; Tho' by
a - ble, He is a - ble

sin op-prest, Go to Him for rest; "Our God is a - ble to de - liv - er thee."

Just Over In The Glory Land

197

JAS. W. ACUFF. Assigned 1944 to R. E. Winsett, Dayton, Tenn. EMMETT S. DEAN.

1. I've a home pre-pared where the saints a-bide, Just o-ver in the
2. I am on my way to those mansions fair, Just o-ver in the
3. What a joy-ful tho't, that my Lord I'll see, Just o-ver in the
4. With the blood-washed throng I will shout and sing, Just o-ver in the

glo-ry-land; And I long to be by my Sav-ior's side, Just
glo-ry-land; There to sing God's praise, and His glo-ry share, Just
glo-ry-land; And with kin-dred saved, there for-ev-er be, Just
glo-ry-land; Glad ho-san-nas to Christ, the Lord and King, Just

REFRAIN.

o-ver in the glo-ry-land. Just o - ver in the glo-ry-land,
Just o-ver, o-ver in the glo-ry-land,

I'll join........ the hap-py an-gel band, Just o-ver in the
I'll join, yes, join the hap-py an-gel band,

glo-ry-land; Just o - - ver in the glo-ry-land, There
Just o-ver, o-ver in the glo-ry-land, There

Just Over In The Glory Land

with........ the might-y host I'll stand, Just o - ver in the glo - ry land.
yes, with

198   Hold to God's Unchanging Hand

F. L. Eiland

Jennie Wilson   Arranged by John T. Benson, Jr.

1. Time is filled with swift transi-tion, Naught of earth unmoved can stand, Build your
2. Trust in Him who will not leave you, What-so-ev-er years may bring, If by
3. Cov - et not this world's vain rich-es, That so rap - id - ly de - cay, Seek to
4. When your journey is com-plet-ed, If to God you have been true, Fair and

CHORUS

hopes on things e - ter - nal, Hold to God's unchanging hand! Hold
earth - ly friends for - sak - en, Still more close-ly to Him cling!
gain the heav'n-ly treas-ures, They will nev-er pass a - way!
bright the home in glo - ry, Your en-rap-tured soul will view! Hold to His hand,

to God's un-chang-ing hand! Hold
Hold to His hand!
to God's un-chang-

Rit.

ing hand! Build your hopes on things e-ter - nal, Hold to God's unchanging hand!

So Many Reasons

David Reece
Jimmie Davis

So man - y rea-sons why I love the Lord, So man-y reasons I can't count them; So man - y rea-sons why I trust His word, So man-y rea-sons I can't count them. One is how He saved me at an old time al- tar, He placed a joy with-in my heart, I know. He changed my life completely, Gave me hope for tomorrow, And that's the reason why I love Him so.

200 The Glory Land Way

Assigned 1943 to R. E. Winsett, Dayton, Tenn.

J. S. T.   J. S. Torbett

1. I'm in the way, the bright and shin-ing way, I'm in the glo-ry land
2. List to the call, the gos-pel call to-day, Get in the glo-ry land
3. On-ward I go, re-joic-ing in His love, I'm in the glo-ry land

way;   Tell-ing the world that Je-sus saves to-day, Yes,
        Wand'rers, come home, oh, hast-en to o-bey, And
glo-ry land way; Soon I shall see Him in that home a-bove, Oh,

CHORUS

I'm in the glo-ry land way. I'm in the glo-ry land
get
I'm   glo-ry land way.

way,   I'm in the glo-ry land way;   Heaven is
glo-ry land way,   glo-ry land way;

near-er, and the way groweth clearer, For I'm in the glo-ry land way.
             glo-ry land way.

He's The Savior Of The World

T. B.
J. D.

Thurman Bunch
Jimmie Davis

If you're burdened down with care, There's a Savior that is near; And the

Sav-ior controls the un - i-verse; In your heart He'll come and dine; He'll be

yours for He is mine, For He's the Sav-ior of the world.

CHORUS

He's the Sav-ior of the world, He has made my life a - new; If you

let Him He will do the same for you. He will turn your night to
Ah
Oo

He's The Savior Of The World

day If you let Him have His way, For He's the Sav-ior of the world.

202

Roll, Jordan, Roll

© 1956 in "Heart Warming Songs" by John T. Benson, Jr., owner

Traditional

Arranged by HAROLD F. HAMMOND

Not too fast

Roll Jor-dan roll, Roll Jor-dan roll I want to go to Heaven when I die,

to hear old Jordan roll.

SOLO

1. O Brothers you ought to have been there yes, my Lord;
2. O Sis-ters you ought to have been there yes, my Lord;
3. O Sin-ners you ought to have been there yes, my Lord;
4. O Mourners you ought to have been there yes, my Lord;

SOLO

A wait-in' in the King-dom To hear old Jor-dan roll. Roll Jor-dan roll,

Roll Jor-dan roll, I want to go to heav'n when I die To hear old Jor-dan roll.

A Beautiful Life

Wm. M. G.   Property Wm. M. Golden, 1918   Wm. M. Golden

1. Each day I'll do .... a gold-en deed, ... By help-ing
2. To be a child .... of God each day, ... My light must
3. The on-ly life .... that will en-dure, ... Is one that's
4. I'll help some-one .... in time of need, ... And jour-ney
5. While go-ing down .... life's wea-ry road, ... I'll try to

those........who are in need;........My life on earth........is but a
shine....... a-long the way;........I'll sing His praise........while a-ges
kind........and good and pure;........And so for God........I'll take my
on........with rap-id speed;........I'll help the sick........the poor and
lift........some trav'ler's load;........I'll try to turn........the night to

span,........And so I'll do..........the best I can, (the best I can).
roll,........And strive to help........some trou-bled soul,(some trou-bled soul).
stand,........Each day I'll lend........a help-ing hand, (a help-ing hand).
weak,........And words of kind - - ness to them speak,(kind words I'll speak).
day,........Make flow-ers bloom........a-long the way, (the lone-ly way).

Refrain

Life's evening sun is sink-ing low, A few more days
Life's evening sun is sinking low, A few more days

and I must go To meet the deeds that I have
and I must go To meet the deeds

A Beautiful Life

done,   Where there will be   no set-ting sun.
that I have done,   Where there will be   no set-ting sun.

204   Hiding In Thee

Rev. William O. Cushing   Ira D. Sankey

1. O safe to the Rock that is high-er than I, My soul in its
2. In calm of the noon-tide, in sor-row's lone hour, In times when temp-
3. How oft in the con-flict, when pressed by the foe, I've fled to my

con-flicts and sor-rows would fly; So sin-ful, so wea-ry, Thine, Thine
ta-tions cast o'er me its pow'r; In tem-pest of life, on its wide
Ref-uge and breathed out my woe; How oft-en, when tri-als like sea-

Chorus

would I be; Thou blest Rock of A-ges, I'm hid-ing in Thee.
heav-ing sea, Thou blest Rock of A-ges, I'm hid-ing in Thee. Hid-ing in
bil-lows roll, I've hid-den in Thee, O Thou Rock of my soul.

Thee, Hid-ing in Thee, Thou blest Rock of A-ges, I'm hid-ing in Thee.

Never Faileth

B. C.

Bud Chambers

1. Oh, when my soul was trou-bled, And I need-ed a friend, I called
2. When I was af-flict-ed, And all hope was gone, I waited

for my loved ones and my dear-est of kin; They all tried to help me,
for an an-swer and suf-fered so long. Then I called on Je-sus,

but to no a-vail; Then I called on Je-sus, for He nev-er
know-ing His will; And He reached down and touched me, for He nev-er

CHORUS

fails. Nev-er fail-eth, Nev-er fail-eth, Je-sus nev-er fails, His
fails.

love is like a riv-er flowing through the hills; Though I stumble, Though I

Never Faileth

fal-ter, He loves me still, Oh I will always love Him, for He nev-er fails.

206   Love Is The Key

W. E. M.   W. Elmo Mercer

1. Love is the key that o-pens wide the door to hap-pi-ness;
2. Love led the Lord to give His Son to save the world from sin;
3. Don't ev-er doubt the way is right, just keep your eyes a-bove;

Love is the key, oh, let it be, and your heart God will bless.
On Cal-v'ry's tree He died for me, and gave me peace with-in.
Trust in the Lord and your re-ward will be to know His Love.

CHORUS

Oh love can mend a bro-ken spir-it, Love can heal the wounded soul,

Oh love in your heart for oth — ers, The key that o-pens all.

When The Roll Is Called Up Yonder

J. M. B.   James M. Black

1. When the trumpet of the Lord shall sound, and time shall be no more, And the
2. On that bright and cloudless morning when the dead in Christ shall rise, And the
3. Let us la-bor for the Mas-ter from the dawn till set-ting sun, Let us

morn-ing breaks e-ter-nal, bright and fair; When the saved of earth shall gather o-ver
glo-ry of His res-ur-rec-tion share, When His chosen ones shall gather to their
talk of all His wondrous love and care, Then when all of life is o-ver and our

FINE   CHORUS

on the oth-er shore,   When the
home beyond the skies, And the roll is called up yonder, I'll be there.
work on earth is done,

roll   is called up yon - der, When the roll   is called up
When the roll is called up yonder, I'll be there,   When the roll is called up

D.S.

yon - der, When the roll   is called up yonder, When the
yonder, I'll be there,   When the roll

I Must Tell Jesus

E. A. H.

Rev. E. A. Hoffman.

1. I must tell Je-sus all of my tri-als; I can-not bear these
2. I must tell Je-sus all of my troub-les; He is a kind, com-
3. Tempted and tried I need a great Sav-ior, One who can help my
4. O how the world to e-vil al-lures me! O how my heart is

bur-dens a lone; In my dis-tress He kind-ly will help me;
pas-sion-ate Friend; If I but ask Him, He will de-liv-er,
bur-dens to bear; I must tell Je-sus, I must tell Je-sus;
tempt-ed to sin! I must tell Je-sus, and He will help me

CHORUS.

He ev-er loves and cares for His own.
Make of my troub-les quick-ly an end. I must tell Je-sus!
He all my cares and sor-rows will share.
O-ver the world the vic-t'ry to win.

I must tell Je-sus! I can-not bear my bur-dens a-lone; I must tell

Je-sus! I must tell Je-sus! Je-sus can help me, Je-sus a-lone. A-MEN.

209 If I Could Hear My Mother Pray Again

James Rowe   J. W. Vaughan, Owner. By Per.   J. W. Vaughan

Slow, with feeling.

1 How sweet and hap-py seem those days of which I dream, When mem-o-
2 She used to pray that I on Je-sus would re-ly, And al-ways
3 With-in the old home-place, her pa-tient, smil-ing face, Was al-ways
4 Her work on earth is done, the life-crown has been won And she will

ry re-calls them now and then! And with that rap-ture sweet my
walk the shin-ing gos-pel way; So trust-ing still His love I
spreading comfort, hope and cheer; And when she used to sing to
be at rest with Him a-bove; And some glad morn-ing, she I

wea-ry heart would beat, If I could hear my mo-ther pray a-gain.
seek that home above, Where I shall meet my mo-ther some glad day.
her e-ter-nal King. It was the songs the an-gels loved to hear.
know will welcome me To that e-ter-nal home of peace and love.

D. S.—so much to me, If I could hear my moth-er pray a-gain.

CHORUS

If I could hear my mo-ther pray a-gain, If I could
If I could on-ly   If I could on-ly

If I could on-ly hear

hear her ten-der voice as then! So glad I'd be, 'twould mean
hap-py I should

hap-py I should be

The Old Gospel Ship

Arr. ALPHUS LEFEVRE

1. I have good news to bring and that is why I sing, All my joys with you
2. Oh, I can scarce-ly wait I know I'll not be late, For I'll spend my time
3. If you're ashamed of me you have no cause to be, For with Christ I am

I'll share; I'm going to take a trip in the Old Gos-pel ship
in pray'r; And when my ship comes in I will leave this world of sin
an heir; If too much fault you find you will sure be left be-hind

CHORUS

And go sail-ing thru the air.
And go sail-ing thru the air.
While I go sail-ing thru the air. Oh, I'm "gonna" take a trip, in the

good Old Gospel Ship, I'm go-ing far be-yond the sky; Oh, I'm "gonna"

shout and sing un-til the heavens ring, When I'm bidding this world good-bye.

Somewhere There's A Friend

211

J. D.

Jimmie Davis

1. Some - where there's a Friend and He's call-ing again, Don't be blue
2. There are times when we all must try so hard not to fall, When it seems

for you know how much He cares. No mat - ter who you are, you can
that our smiles have turned to frowns, There is One that I know and to

be a shin-ing star, but don't for-get that your burdens He will share.
Him I would go. He will love you when the world has turned you down.

CHORUS

Somewhere there's a Friend who'll go to the end. All the way to judg-ment day

I've been told. He will share all your heart - aches and com - fort

Somewhere There's A Friend

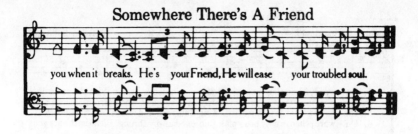

you when it breaks. He's your Friend, He will ease your troubled soul.

I Know Whom I Have Believed

DANIEL W. WHITTLE (EL NATHAN)   JAMES McGRANAHAN

1. I know not why God's wondrous grace To me He hath made known,
2. I know not how this sav-ing faith To me He did im-part,
3. I know not how the Spir-it moves, Con-vinc-ing men of sin,
4. I know not when my Lord may come, At night or noon-day fair,

Nor why, un-wor-thy, Christ in love Re-deemed me for His own.
Nor how be-liev-ing in His Word Wrought peace within my heart.
Re-veal-ing Je-sus thro' the Word, Cre-at-ing faith in Him.
Nor if I'll walk the vale with Him, Or "meet Him in the air."

CHORUS

But "I know whom I have be-liev-ed, and am per-suad-ed that He is

a-ble To keep that which I've com-mit-ted Un-to Him a-gainst that day."

Sabine Baring-Gould.   Arthur Sullivan.

1. On - ward, Chris-tian sol - diers! March-ing as to war, With the cross of
2. Like a might - y ar - my Moves the Church of God; Broth-ers, we are
3. Crowns and thrones may per-ish, King-doms rise and wane; But the Church of
4. On - ward, then, ye peo - ple! Join our hap-py throng, Blend with ours your

Je - sus Go - ing on be - fore. Christ, the roy - al Mas - ter,
tread - ing Where the saints have trod; We are not di - vid - ed,
Je - sus Con-stant will re - main; Gates of hell can nev - er
voic - es In the tri-umph-song; Glo - ry, laud, and hon - or,

Leads a-gainst the foe; For-ward in - to bat - tle, See His ban-ners go!
All one bod - y we, One in hope and doc - trine, One in char - i - ty.
'Gainst that Church pre-vail; We have Christ's own prom-ise, Which can nev-er fail.
Un - to Christ the King, This thro' count-less a - ges Men and an-gels sing.

CHORUS.

On - ward, Chris - tian sol - diers! March-ing as to war,

With the cross of Je - sus Go - ing on be - fore.

Will You Be Saved?

214

L. G.
J. D.

Lari Goss
Jimmie Davis

1. The har-vest is past, the sum-mer is end-ed, Oh
2. He stands at the door, the Sav-ior is plead-ing, Oh

bro-ther, will you be saved? Time now is fleeting, the
bro-ther, will you be saved? Now is the time, the

moments are pass-ing, Oh brother, will you be saved?
day of sal-va-tion, Oh brother, will you be saved?

CHORUS

Will you be saved from your sin? Will you let Je-sus come in?

Look up in pray'r, He'll meet you there, Oh, brother, will you be saved?

The Church in the Wildwood

W. S. P.

Dr. Wm. S. Pitts

1. There's a church in the val-ley by the wild-wood, No love-li-er
2. Oh, come to the church in the wild-wood, To the trees where the
3. How sweet on a clear Sab-bath morn-ing, To list to the
4. From the church in the val-ley by the wild-wood, When day fades a-

spot in the dale; No place is so dear to my child-hood As the
wild flow-ers bloom; Where the part-ing hymn will be chant-ed, We will
clear ring-ing bell; Its tones so sweet-ly are call-ing, Oh,
way in-to night, I would fain from this spot of my child-hood Wing my

D.S.—*No spot is so dear to my child-hood As the*

Fine Chorus

lit-tle brown church in the vale.
weep by the side of the tomb.
come to the church in the vale.
way to the man-sions of light.

Come to the

Oh, come, come, come, come, come, come,

lit-tle brown church in the vale.

D.S.

church in the wild - wood, Oh, come to the church in the vale;
come, come, come, come, come, come, come, come, come, come, come, come, come;

Each Step I Take

216

W. E. M.

W. Elmo Mercer

1. Each step I take my Sav-iour goes be-fore me, And with His lov-ing hand
2. At times I feel my faith be-gin to wa-ver, When up a-head I see
3. I trust in God, no mat-ter come what may, For life e-ter-nal

He leads the way. And with each breath I whis-per "I a-dore Thee;" Oh, what
a chas-m wide, It's then I turn and look up to my Sav-iour, I am
is in His hand, He holds the key that o-pens up the way, That will

Rit. CHORUS

joy to walk with Him each day.
strong when He is by my side. Each step I take I know that He will
lead me to the promised land.

guide me; To high-er ground He ev-er leads me on. Un-til some day the last

Rit.

step will be tak-en, Each step I take just leads me clos-er home.

Jesus, I Come

W. T. Sleeper   Geo. C. Stebbins

1. Out of my bond-age, sor-row and night, Je-sus, I come, Je-sus, I come;
2. Out of my shame-ful fail-ure and loss, Je-sus, I come, Je-sus, I come;
3. Out of un-rest and ar - ro-gant pride, Je-sus, I come, Je-sus, I come;
4. Out of the fear and dread of the tomb, Je-sus, I come, Je-sus, I come;

In - to Thy free-dom, glad-ness and light, Je-sus, I come to Thee;
In - to the glo - rious gain of Thy cross, Je-sus, I come to Thee;
In - to Thy bless - ed will to a - bide, Je-sus, I come to Thee;
In - to the joy and light of Thy home, Je-sus, I come to Thee;

Out of my sick-ness in - to Thy health, Out of my want and in - to Thy wealth,
Out of earth's sorrows in-to Thy balm, Out of life's storms and in - to Thy calm,
Out of my - self to dwell in Thy love, Out of de-spair in-to rap-tures a-bove,
Out of the depths of ru - in un - told, In - to the peace of Thy sheltering fold,

Out of my sin and in - to Thy-self, Je - sus, I come to Thee.
Out of dis-tress to ju - bi - lant psalm, Je - sus, I come to Thee.
Up-ward for aye on wings like a dove, Je - sus, I come to Thee.
Ev - er Thy glo - rious face to be-hold, Je - sus, I come to Thee.

I am Praying for You

S. O'Maley Cluff.

Ira D. Sankey.

1. I have a Sav - ior, He's plead - ing in glo - ry, A dear, lov-ing Sav-
2. I have a Fa - ther; to me He has giv - en A hope for e - ter-
3. I have a robe: 'tis re - splend - ent in whiteness, A - wait - ing in glo-
4. When Jesus has found you, tell oth-ers the sto - ry, That my lov - ing Sav-

ior tho' earth-friends be few; And now He is watch - ing in ten - der - ness
ni - ty, bless - ed and true; And soon will He call me to meet Him in
ry my won - der - ing view; Oh, when I re - ceive it all shin - ing in
ior is your Sav - ior too; Then pray that your Sav - ior may bring them to

CHORUS.

o'er me, And, oh, that my Sav-ior were your Sav-ior too.
heav - en, But, oh, that He'd let me bring you with me too!   For you I am
brightness, Dear friend. could I see you re-ceiv - ing one too!
glo - ry, And pray'r will be answered—'twas answered for you!

praying, For you I am praying, For you I am praying, I'm pray-ing for you.

219 Seeking the Lost

W. A. O. USED BY PERMISSION OF MRS. W. A. OGDEN. W. A. Ogden.

M. 72 = ♩.

1. Seek-ing the lost, yes, kind-ly en-treat-ing Wan-der-ers
2. Seek-ing the lost, and point-ing to Je-sus, Souls that are
3. Thus I would go on mis-sions of mer-cy, Fol-low-ing

on the moun-tain a-stray; "Come un-to Me," His
weak and hearts that are sore; Lead-ing them forth in
Christ from day un-to day; Cheer-ing the faint, and

mes-sage re-peat-ing, Words of the Mas-ter speak-ing to-day.
ways of sal-va-tion, Show-ing the path to life ev-er-more.
rais-ing the fall-en; Point-ing the lost to Je-sus, the Way.

CHORUS.

{ Go-ing a-far up-on the moun-tain,
{ In-to the fold of my Re-deem-er,

{ Go-ing a-far.......... up-on the moun - tain,.... Bring-ing the
{ In-to the fold......... of my Re-deem-er,....... Je-sus, the

1.   2.

Bring-ing the wan-d'rer back a-gain, back a-gain, }
Je-sus, the Lamb for sin-ners (Omit...............) } slain, for sin-ners slain.

wan - - - d'rer back a-gain,....... }
Lamb.......... for sin-ners (Omit.......) } slain..........

220   Take My Hand, Precious Lord

1 & 2 Ver. & Mel. Thomas A. Dorsey   Arr. by R. E. Winsett. by per. T. A. D.
Arr. Copyright 1939, in "Sacred Jewels," by R. E. Winsett, Dayton, Tenn.
3 Ver. Copyright, 1949, by R. E. Winsett, "Fount Of Blessings."

1. When my way grow-eth drear, pre-cious Lord, lin-ger near, When my life
2. When the shad-ows ap-pear, and the night draw-eth near, And the day
3. Near-ing life-jour-ney's end, be my Guide, be my Friend, Give me strength

is al-most gone; Hear my cry, hear my call, hold my hand
is past and gone; At the riv-er I stand, guide my feet
Lord, to o-ver come; I'll not go all a-lone, for by grace

lest I fall;
hold my hand; Take my hand, pre-cious Lord, lead me home.
I'm Thine own;

D. S. To the light; Take my hand, pre-cious Lord, Lead me home.

REFRAIN

Pre-cious Lord, take my hand, lead me on, let me stand, I am tired,

I am weak, I am worn; Thru the storm, thru the night, lead me on,

I Cannot Find The Way Alone

A. E. B.

Albert E. Brumley

1. As I jour-ney thru this vale of sor-row, The way seems so strange and un-known. Lord, I need a help-ing hand to bor-row, for I can-not find the way a-lone.

2. I have no oth-er friend to guide me, And I am so weak and un-done, Walk a lit-tle clos-er Lord, be-side me, for I can-not find the way a-lone.

3. When the rag-ing storms of life con-found me, Dear Lord, wilt Thou keep me Thine own, Let me feel Thy pre-cious arms a-round me, for I can-not find the way a-lone.

CHORUS

I can-not find the way with-out Thee, Dear Lord, look down from Thy throne. And make Thy light to shine a-bout me, For I can-not find the way a-lone.

222   Let Him In

Rev. J. B. Atchinson.   E. O. Excell.

1. There's a Stran-ger at the door.   Let   Him in;
2. O - pen now to Him your heart,   Let   Him in;
3. Hear you now His lov - ing voice?   Let   Him in;
4. Now ad - mit the heav'n-ly Guest,   Let   Him in;
   Let the Savior in,   Let the Savior in;

He has been there oft be - fore,   Let   Him in:
If you wait He will de - part,   Let   Him in;
Now, oh, now make Him your choice,   Let   Him in;
He will make for you a feast,   Let   Him in;
   Let the Savior in,   Let the Savior in;

Let Him in, ere He is gone,   Let Him in, the Ho - ly   One,
Let Him in, He is your Friend,   He your soul will sure de - fend,
He is stand-ing at your door,   Joy to you He will re - store,
He will speak your sins for - giv'n,   And when earth-ties all are riv'n,

Je - sus Christ, the Fa-ther's Son,   Let   Him in.
He will keep you to the end,   Let   Him in.
And His name you will a - dore,   Let   Him in.
He will take you home to Heav'n,   Let   Him in.
   Let the Savior in,   Let the Savior in.

The Home over There

D. W. C. Huntington.

Tullius C. O'Kane.

M. 96 = ♩

1. O think of the home o-ver there, By the side of the riv-er of light,
2. O think of the friends o-ver there, Who be-fore us the journey have trod,
3. My Sav-ior is now o-ver there, There my kindred and friends are at rest,
4. I'll soon be at home o-ver there, For the end of my jour-ney I see;

over there,

Where the saints, all immortal and fair, Are robed in their garments of white.
Of the songs that they breathe on the air, In their home in the pal-ace of God.
Then a-way from my sor-row and care, Let me fly to the land of the blest.
Man-y dear to my heart, o-ver there, Are watching and waiting for me.

over there.

REFRAIN.

O-ver there, o-ver there,

Over there, over there,

O think of the home o-ver there;
O think of the friends o-ver there;
My Sav-ior is now o-ver there;
I'll soon be at home o-ver there;

over there;

O-ver there, o-ver there, o-ver there,

Over there, over there,

O think of the home o-ver there.
O think of the friends o-ver there.
My Sav-ior is now o-ver there.
I'll soon be at home o-ver there.

224 When They Ring The Golden Bells

Arr. Copyright, 1946, in "Sacred Service Songs" by R. E. Winsett, Dayton, Tenn.

Arr. R. E. Winsett

1. There's a land be-yond the riv-er That we call the sweet for-ev-er, And we
2. We shall know no sin or sorrow In that ha-ven of to-morrow, When our
3. When our days shall know their number, When in death we sweetly slumber, When the

on-ly reach that shore by faith's decree; One by one we'll gain the portals There to
barque shall sail beyond the sil-ver sea; We shall on-ly know the bless-ing Of our
King commands the spir-it to be free; Nev-er-more with anguish lad-en, We shall

FINE

dwell with the im-mortals,
Fa-ther's sweet caressing, When they ring the gold-en bells for you and me, you and me.
reach that love-ly aidenn,

D. S.-yond the shin-ing riv-er,

CHORUS

Don't you hear the bells now ringing? Don't you hear the angels sing-ing? 'Tis the

D.S.

glo-ry hal-le-lu-jah Ju-bi-lee, Ju-bi-lee. In that far-off sweet forev-er, Just be-

The Unclouded Day

Rev. J. K. A.

Rev. J. K. Alwood

1. O they tell me of a home far be-yond the skies, O they
2. O they tell me of a home where my friends have gone, O they
3. O they tell me of the King in His beau-ty there, And they
4. O they tell me that He smiles on His chil-dren there, And His

tell me of a home far a - way; O they tell me of a home
tell me of that land far a - way; Where the tree of life
tell me that mine eyes shall be-hold; Where He sits on the throne
smile drives their sor-row all a - way; And they tell me that no tears

D. S.-O they tell me of a home

FINE

where no storm - clouds rise, O they tell me of an un-cloud - ed day.
in e - ter - nal bloom, Sheds its fragrance thro' the un-cloud - ed day.
that is whit - er than snow, In the cit - y that is made of gold.
ev - er come a - gain, In that love - ly land of un-cloud - ed day.

where no storm - clouds rise, O they tell me of an un-cloud-ed day.

CHORUS

D.S.

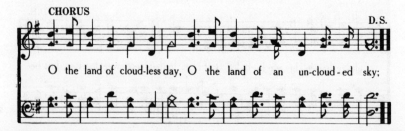

O the land of cloud-less day, O the land of an un-cloud - ed sky;

Tell Me the Story of Jesus

Fanny J. Crosby.

Jno. R. Sweney.

M. 100 = ♩

1. Tell me the sto - ry of Je - sus, Write on my heart ev - 'ry word;
2. Fast-ing a-lone in the des - ert, Tell of the days that are passed,
3. Tell of the cross where they nailed Him, Writh-ing in an - guish and pain;

CHO.—*Tell me the sto - ry of Je - sus, Write on my heart ev - 'ry word;*

FINE.

Tell me the sto - ry most pre - cious, Sweet-est that ev - er was heard.
How for our sins He was tempt - ed, Yet was tri-um-phant at last.
Tell of the grave where they laid Him, Tell how He liv - eth a - gain.

Tell me the sto - ry most pre-cious, Sweet-est that ev - er was heard.

Tell how the an - gels, in cho - rus, Sang as they wel-comed His birth,
Tell of the years of His la - bor, Tell of the sor - row He bore,
Love in that sto - ry so ten - der, Clear - er than ev - er I see;

D.C. for Cho.

"Glo - ry to God in the high - est! Peace and good ti - dings to earth."
He was de-spised and af - flict - ed, Home-less, re - ject-ed and poor.
Stay, let me weep while you whis - per, Love paid the ran-som for me.

Work, For The Night Is Coming

Annie L. Coghill

Lowell Mason

1. Work, for the night is com-ing, Work thru the morning hours; Work while the
2. Work, for the night is com-ing, Work thru the sun-ny noon; Fill bright-est
3. Work, for the night is com-ing, Un-der the sun-set skies; While the bright

dew is sparkling, Work 'mid springing flow'rs; Work when the day grows bright-er,
hours with la-bor, Rest comes sure and soon. Give ev-'ry fly-ing min-ute
tints are glow-ing, Work, for daylight flies. Work till the last beam fad-eth,

Work in the glowing sun; Work, for the night is coming, When man's work is done.
Something to keep in store: Work, for the night is coming, When man works no more.
Fad-eth to shine no more; Work, while the night is dark'ning, When man's work is o'er.

228

Rock Of Ages

Augustus M. Toplady

Thomas Hastings

1. Rock of A-ges, cleft for me, Let me hide my-self in Thee;
2. Could my tears for-ev-er flow, Could my zeal no lan-guor know,
3. While I draw this fleet-ing breath, When my eyes shall close in death,

Let the wa-ter and the blood, From Thy wound-ed side which flowed,
These for sin could not a-tone; Thou must save, and Thou a-lone:
When I rise to worlds un-known, And be-hold Thee on Thy throne,

Rock Of Ages

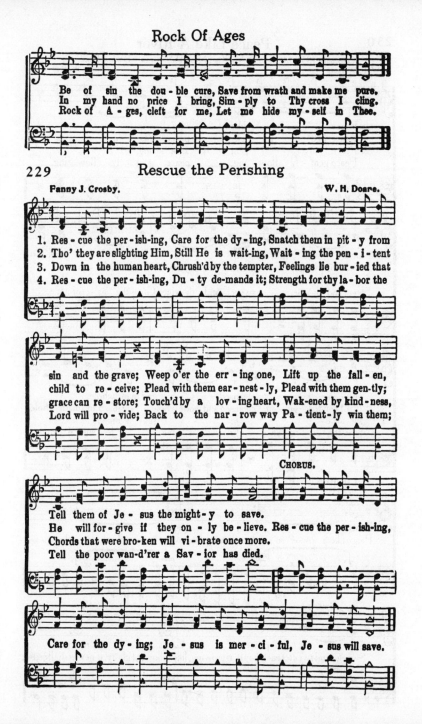

Be of sin the dou - ble cure, Save from wrath and make me pure.
In my hand no price I bring, Sim - ply to Thy cross I cling.
Rock of A - ges, cleft for me, Let me hide my - self in Thee.

229

Rescue the Perishing

Fanny J. Crosby.

W. H. Doane.

1. Res - cue the per - ish - ing, Care for the dy - ing, Snatch them in pit - y from
2. Tho' they are slighting Him, Still He is wait - ing, Wait - ing the pen - i - tent
3. Down in the human heart, Chrush'd by the tempter, Feelings lie bur - ied that
4. Res - cue the per - ish - ing, Du - ty de-mands it; Strength for thy la - bor the

sin and the grave; Weep o'er the err - ing one, Lift up the fall - en,
child to re - ceive; Plead with them ear - nest - ly, Plead with them gen - tly;
grace can re - store; Touch'd by a lov - ing heart, Wak-ened by kind - ness,
Lord will pro - vide; Back to the nar - row way Pa - tient - ly win them;

CHORUS.

Tell them of Je - sus the might - y to save.
He will for - give if they on - ly be - lieve. Res - cue the per - ish - ing,
Chords that were bro - ken will vi - brate once more.
Tell the poor wan-d'rer a Sav - ior has died.

Care for the dy - ing; Je - sus is mer - ci - ful, Je - sus will save.

230 Peace Like A River

W. B. Walbert   James D. Walbert

1. Peace like a riv - er
Peace like a riv - er, peace like a riv - er
2. Peace gent - ly flow - ing,
Peace gent - ly flow - ing, peace gent - ly flow - ing,

Flows thru my soul; I've been for-
Flows thru my soul, flows thru my soul; I've been for - giv - en,
Sweet and di - vine; Gives the as-
Sweet and di - vine, sweet and di - vine; Gives the as - sur - ance,

giv - en, cleansed and made whole.
I've been for - giv - en, cleansed and made whole, cleansed and made whole.
sur - ance Je - sus is mine.
gives the as - sur - ance Je - sus is mine, Je - sus is mine.

CHORUS

Peace, peace,
Peace like a riv - er so gently is flowing, how sweet to my soul is this marvelous peace,

Sweet peace God's peace;
Sweeter and sweeter each day it is growing, like billows of glo - ry, it nev-er shall cease;

Peace Like A River

231 We'll Never Say Goodbye

L. R. I.

Lois R. Irwin

1. We will nev - er say good-bye o - ver yon-der in the sky, We will be
2. There will be no sor row there at that meet-ing in the air When the dead
3. Some glad hap- py day we'll meet, at the bless-ed Sav-ior's feet When our race

to- geth- er then, thru out all e - ter - ni - ty; What a glad re - un - ion
in Christ shall rise we will meet them in the skies. We'll be free from death and
on earth is done and the crown of life we've won Christ will welcome us to

day when the Sav-ior's face we'll see
sin, life will on - ly then be - gin   Over there where we'll never say goodbye.
stay where we'll spend an endless day

CHORUS

We will nev - er say good-bye, o - ver yon-der in the sky, What a

glad day when we're home to stay   Sad fare-well will on - ly be just a

We'll Never Say Goodbye

fad-ed mem-o-ry, O-ver there where we'll nev-er say good-bye.

232 Ship Ahoy

M. J. Cartwright

D. B. Towner

'Effective Solo

1. I was drift-ing a-way on life's pit-i-less sea, And the
2. 'Twas the "Old ship of Zi-on," thus sail-ing a-long, All a-
3. The good Cap-tain com-mand-ed a boat to be low'red, And with
4. O soul, sink-ing down 'neath sin's mer-ci-less wave, The strong

an-gry waves threatened my ru-in to be, When a-way at my side, there I
board her seemed joyous, I heard their sweet song; And the Captain's kind ear, ev-er
ten-der com-pas-sion He took me on board; And I'm hap-py to-day, all my
arm of our Cap-tain is might-y to save; Then trust Him to-day, no

dim-ly des-cried A state-ly old ves-sel, and loud-ly I cried:
read-y to hear, Caught my wail of dis-tress, as I cried out in fear:
sins washed a-way In the blood of my Sav-ior, and now I can say:
long-er de-lay, Board the old ship of Zi-on, and shout on your way:

"Ship a-hoy! Ship a-hoy!" And loud-ly I cried: "Ship a-hoy!"
"Ship a-hoy! Ship a-hoy!" As I cried out in fear: "Ship a-hoy!"
"Bless the Lord!" Bless the Lord!" From my soul I can say: Bless the Lord!"
"Je-sus saves! Je-sus saves!" Shout and sing on your way: "Jesus saves!"

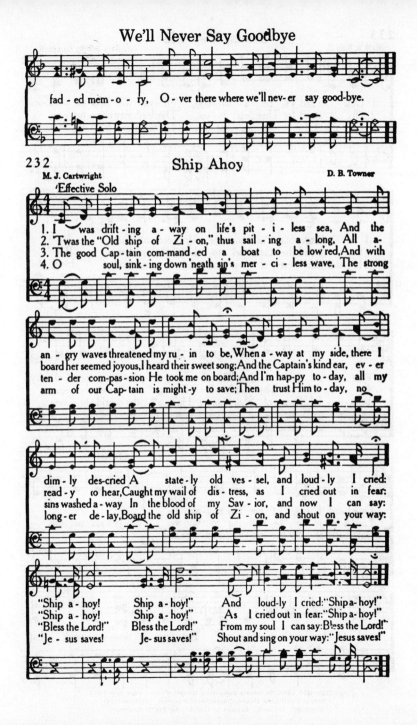

233 Jesus, Use Me

Jack & Billy C.

Jack & Billy Campbell

1. Dear Lord I'll be a wit-ness, If you will help my weak-ness,
2. I'll stand for Thee dear Je-sus, 'Tho death may come my way,
3. He's the Lil-y of the val-ley, The bright and morn-ing Star,

I know that I'm not wor-thy Lord of Thee; By
I'll spread the Gos-pel to the fall-en here; But
He's the fair-est of ten thou-sand to my soul; He's the

eyes of faith I see Thee, Up-on the cross of Cal-v'ry,
if it be Thy will Lord, To go a-cross the sea,
beau-ti-ful Rose of Shar-on, He's all the world to me,

CHORUS

Dear Lord I cry, let me Thy serv-ant be.
Lord help me to be will-ing to say yes. Je-sus use me,
But best of all, He is my com-ing King.

and O Lord don't re-fuse me, For sure-ly there's a work that

Jesus, Use Me

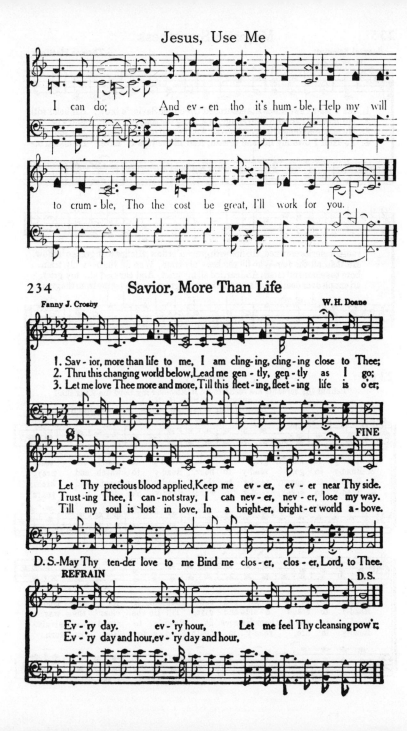

I can do; And ev-en tho it's hum-ble, Help my will

to crum-ble, Tho the cost be great, I'll work for you.

234 Savior, More Than Life

Fanny J. Crosby

W. H. Doane

1. Sav-ior, more than life to me, I am cling-ing, cling-ing close to Thee;
2. Thru this changing world below, Lead me gen-tly, gen-tly as I go;
3. Let me love Thee more and more, Till this fleet-ing, fleet-ing life is o'er;

FINE

Let Thy precious blood applied, Keep me ev-er, ev-er near Thy side.
Trust-ing Thee, I can-not stray, I can nev-er, nev-er, lose my way.
Till my soul is lost in love, In a bright-er, bright-er world a-bove.

D. S.—May Thy ten-der love to me Bind me clos-er, clos-er, Lord, to Thee.

REFRAIN

D.S.

Ev-'ry day. ev-'ry hour, Let me feel Thy cleansing pow'r,
Ev-'ry day and hour, ev-'ry day and hour,

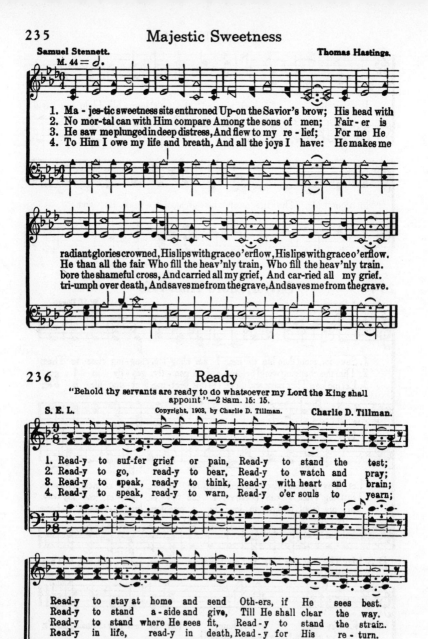

235

Majestic Sweetness

Samuel Stennett.

Thomas Hastings.

M. 44 = ♩.

1. Ma - jes-tic sweetness sits enthroned Up-on the Savior's brow; His head with
2. No mor-tal can with Him compare Among the sons of men; Fair - er is
3. He saw me plunged in deep distress, And flew to my re - lief; For me He
4. To Him I owe my life and breath, And all the joys I have: He makes me

radiant glories crowned, His lips with grace o'erflow, His lips with grace o'erflow.
He than all the fair Who fill the heav'nly train, Who fill the heav'nly train.
bore the shameful cross, And carried all my grief, And car-ried all my grief.
tri-umph over death, And saves me from the grave, And saves me from the grave.

236

Ready

"Behold thy servants are ready to do whatsoever my Lord the King shall
appoint."—2 Sam. 15: 15.

S. E. L.

Copyright, 1903, by Charlie D. Tillman.

Charlie D. Tillman.

1. Read-y to suf-fer grief or pain, Read-y to stand the test;
2. Read-y to go, read-y to bear, Read-y to watch and pray;
3. Read-y to speak, read-y to think, Read-y with heart and brain;
4. Read-y to speak, read-y to warn, Read-y o'er souls to yearn;

Read-y to stay at home and send Oth-ers, if He sees best.
Read-y to stand a - side and give, Till He shall clear the way.
Read-y to stand where He sees fit, Read-y to stand the strain.
Read-y in life, read-y in death, Read-y for His re - turn.

Ready

Read-y to go, read-y to stay, Read-y my place to fill;

Read-y for ser-vice, low-ly or great, Read-y to do His will.

237   I Need Thee Every Hour

Mrs. Annie S. Hawks   Rev. Robert Lowry

1. I need Thee ev - 'ry hour, Most gra - cious Lord; No ten - der voice like
2. I need Thee ev - 'ry hour, Stay Thou near by; Temp-ta-tions lose their
3. I need Thee ev - 'ry hour, In joy or pain; Come quick-ly and a-
4. I need Thee ev - 'ry hour, Most Ho - ly One; O make me Thine in-

Thine Can peace af - ford.
pow'r When Thou art nigh.   I need Thee, O I need Thee; Ev-'ry hour I
bide, Or life is vain.
deed, Thou bless - ed Son.

Chorus

need Thee! O bless me now, my Sav - ior, I come to Thee!

Touch The Hand Of The Lord

C. G.   Charles Goodman
J. D.   Jimmie Davis

In a crowd, or a-lone, ev-en far, far from home, Reach out, touch the hand of the

Lord;   On a bus-y thoroughfare, you can e - ven find Him there, Reach out,

CHORUS

touch the hand of the Lord.   Touch the hand that was nailed to a cru-el tree,

A hand that has pow'r, yet so ten-der it can be. And when trou-bles as-

Ah

sail   you, this hand will nev - er fail you, Reach out, touch the

Ah

Touch The Hand Of The Lord

FINE

Hand of the Lord. Reach out, touch the hand of the Lord.

239

A Child Was Born

J. M.
J. D.

Jack Mainord
Jimmie Davis

1. A Child was born in Beth-le-hem, 'Twas Je-sus, our Sav-ior and King;
2. A ti-ny lit-tle in-fant Boy, So sweet and ten-der was He,
3. He is the Sav-ior of the world Who died on the cru-el tree;

The star of Beth-le-hem shone bright, Great tidings of joy did bring.
Be-came the Sav-ior of all men; The songs of this love we sing.
Let's not for-get His pre-cious blood Was shed for you and me.

CHORUS

He had a man-ger for a bed, He slept up-on the hay;

His birth is worshipped by all men Each won-der-ful Christ-mas day.

Julia Ward Howe

William Steffe

1. Mine eyes have seen the glo-ry of the com-ing of the Lord; He is
2. I have seen Him in the watch-fires of a hundred circling camps; They have
3. He has sounded forth the trumpet that shall nev-er sound re-treat; He is
4. In the beau-ty of the lil-ies Christ was born a-cross the sea, With a

trampling out the vintage where the grapes of wrath are stored; He hath loosed the
build-ed Him an al-tar in the evening dews and damps; I can read His
sift-ing out the hearts of men be-fore His judgment seat. O be swift, my
glo-ry in His bos-om that trans-fig-ures you and me; As He died to

fate-ful lightning of His ter-ri-ble swift sword; His truth is marching on.
righteous sentence by the dim and flar-ing lamps; His day is marching on.
soul, to an-swer Him! be ju-bi-lant, my feet! Our God is marching on.
make men ho-ly, let us die to make men free; While God is marching on.

Glo-ry! glo-ry, hal-le-lu-jah! Glo-ry! glo-ry, hal-le-lu-jah! His truth is marching on.
Glo-ry! glo-ry, hal-le-lu-jah! Glo-ry! glo-ry, hal-le-lu-jah! His day is marching on.
Glo-ry! glo-ry, hal-le-lu-jah! Glo-ry! glo-ry, hal-le-lu-jah! Our God is marching on.
Glo-ry! glo-ry, hal-le-lu-jah! Glo-ry! glo-ry, hal-le-lu-jah! While God is marching on.

RESPONSIVE READINGS

241   Adoration

Psalms 8

O Lord our Lord, how excellent is thy name in all the earth!

Who hast set thy glory above the heavens.

Out of the mouth of babes and sucklings hast thou ordained strength because of thine enemies, that thou mightest still the enemy and the avenger.

When I consider thy heavens, the work of thy fingers, the moon and the stars, which thou hast ordained;

What is man, that thou art mindful of him? and the son of man, that thou visitest him?

For thou hast made him a little lower than the angels, and hast crowned him with glory and honour.

Thou madest him to have dominion over the works of thy hands; thou hast put all things under his feet:

All sheep and oxen, yea, and the beasts of the field;

The fowl of the air, and the fish of the sea, and whatsoever passeth through the paths of the seas.

O Lord our Lord, how excellent is thy name in all the earth!

242   Praise

Psalms 96: 1-10

O sing unto the Lord a new song: sing unto the Lord, all the earth.

Sing unto the Lord, bless his name; shew forth his salvation from day to day.

Declare his glory among the heathen, his wonders. among all people.

For the Lord is great, and greatly to be praised: he is to be feared above all gods.

For all the gods of the nations are idols: but the Lord made the heavens.

Honour and majesty are before him: strength and beauty are in his sanctuary.

Give unto the Lord, O ye kindreds of the people, give unto the Lord glory and strength.

Give unto the Lord the glory due unto his name: bring an offering, and come into his courts.

O worship the Lord in the beauty of holiness: fear before him, all the earth.

Say among the heathen that the Lord reigneth: the world also shall be established that it shall not be moved: he shall judge the people righteously.

Psalms 23; John 10:11, 14-17   *Luke 4: 38-40; 17: 12-17, 19*

The Lord is my shepherd; I shall not want.

He maketh me to lie down in green pastures: he leadeth me beside the still waters.

He restoreth my soul: he leadeth me in the paths of righteousness for his name's sake.

Yea, though I walk through the valley of the shadow of death, I will fear no evil: for thou art with me; thy rod and thy staff they comfort me.

Thou preparest a table before me in the presence of mine enemies: thou anointest my head with oil; my cup runneth over.

Surely goodness and mercy shall follow me all the days of my life: and I will dwell in the house of the Lord for ever.

I am the good shepherd: the good shepherd giveth his life for the sheep. . . . I am the good shepherd, and know my sheep, and am known of mine.

As the Father knoweth me, even so know I the Father: and I lay down my life for the sheep.

And other sheep I have, which are not of this fold: them also I must bring, and they shall hear my voice; and there shall be one fold, and one shepherd.

Therefore doth my Father love me, because I lay down my life, that I might take it again.

And he arose out of the synagogue, and entered into Simon's house.

And Simon's wife's mother was taken with a great fever; and they besought him for her.

And he stood over her, and rebuked the fever; and it left her: and immediately she arose and ministered unto them.

Now when the sun was setting, all they that had any sick with divers diseases brought them unto him;

And he laid his hands on every one of them, and healed them.

And as he entered into a certain village, there met him ten men that were lepers, which stood afar off:

And they lifted up their voices, and said, Jesus, Master, have mercy on us.

And when he saw them, he said unto them, Go shew yourselves unto the priests. And it came to pass, that, as they went, they were cleansed.

And one of them, when he saw that he was healed, turned back, and with a loud voice glorified God,

And fell down on his face at his feet, giving him thanks: and he was a Samaritan.

And Jesus answering said, Were there not ten cleansed? but where are the nine?

And he said unto him, Arise, go thy way: thy faith hath made thee whole.

My Light

Psalms 27: 1-11, 13-14

The Lord is my light and my salvation; whom shall I fear? the Lord is the strength of my life; of whom shall I be afraid?

When the wicked, even mine enemies and my foes, came upon me to eat up my flesh, they stumbled and fel'.

Though an host should encamp against me, my heart shall not fear: though war should rise against me, in this will I be confident.

One thing have I desired of the Lord, that will I seek after;

That I may dwell in the house of the Lord all the days of my life, to behold the beauty of the Lord, and to enquire in his temple.

For in the time of trouble he shall hide me in his pavilion:

In the secret of his tabernacle shall he hide me; he shall set me up upon a rock.

And now shall mine head be lifted up above mine enemies round about me:

Therefore will I offer in his tabernacle sacrifices of joy; I will sing, yea, I will sing praises unto the Lord.

Hear, O Lord, when I cry with my voice: have mercy also upon me, and answer me.

When thou saidst, Seek ye my face; my heart said unto thee, Thy face, Lord, will I seek.

Hide not thy face far from me; put not thy servant away in anger: thou hast been my help; leave me not, neither forsake me, O God of my salvation.

When my father and my mother forsake me, then the Lord will take me up.

Teach me thy way, O Lord, and lead me in a plain path, because of mine enemies.

I had fainted, unless I had believed to see the goodness of the Lord in the land of the living.

Wait on the Lord: be of good courage, and he shall strengthen thine heart: wait I say, on the Lord.

246   My Help

Psalms 121

I will lift up mine eyes unto the hills, from whence cometh my help.

My help cometh from the Lord, which made heaven and earth.

He will not suffer thy foot to be moved: he that keepeth thee will not slumber.

Behold, he that keepeth Israel shall neither slumber nor sleep.

The Lord is thy keeper: the Lord is thy shade upon thy right hand.

The sun shall not smite thee by day, nor the moon by night.

The Lord shall preserve thee from all evil: he shall preserve thy soul.

The Lord shall preserve thy going out and thy coming in from this time forth, and even for evermore.

247 Christ Foretold

The people that walked in darkness have seen a great light:

They that dwell in the land of the shadow of death, upon them hath the light shined.

Thou hast multiplied the nation, and not increased the joy:

They joy before thee according to the joy in harvest, and as men rejoice when they divide the spoil.

For thou hast broken the yoke of his burden, and the staff of his shoulder, the rod of his oppressor, as in the day of Midian.

For every battle of the warrior is with confused noise, and garments rolled in blood; but this shall be with burning and fuel of fire.

For unto us a child is born, unto us a son is given: and the government shall be upon his shoulder:

And his name shall be called W o n d e r f u l , Counsellor, The mighty God, The everlasting Father, The Prince of Peace.

Of the increase of his government and peace there shall be no end, upon the throne of David, and upon his kingdom, to order it, and to establish it with judgment and with justice from henceforth even for ever.

The zeal of the Lord of hosts will perform this.

The Lord himself shall give you a sign;

Behold, a virgin shall conceive, and bear a son, and shall call his name Immanuel.

248 Christ Fulfilling

And she brought forth her firstborn son, and wrapped him in swaddling clothes, and laid him in a manger; because there was no room for them in the inn.

And there were in the same country shepherds abiding in the field, keeping watch over their flock by night.

And, lo, the angel of the Lord came upon them, and the glory of the Lord shone round about them: and they were sore afraid.

And the angel said unto them, Fear not: for, behold, I bring you good tidings of great joy, which shall be to all people.

For unto you is born this day in the city of David a Saviour, which is Christ the Lord.

And this shall be a sign unto you; Ye shall find the babe wrapped in swaddling clothes, lying in a manger.

And suddenly there was with the angel a multitude of the heavenly host praising God, and saying,

Glory to God in the highest, and on earth peace, good will toward men.

And it came to pass, as the angels were gone away from them into heaven, the shepherds said one to another, Let us now go even unto Bethlehem, and see this thing which is come to pass.

And they came with haste, and found Mary, and Joseph, and the babe lying in a manger.

Matthew 11: 28-30; Isaiah 55: 1-3; John 6: 37-38, 40

Come unto me, all ye that labour and are heavy laden, and I will give you rest.

Take my yoke upon you, and learn of me; for I am meek and lowly in heart:

And ye shall find rest unto your souls.

For my yoke is easy, and my burden is light.

Ho, every one that thirsteth, come ye to the waters, and he that hath no money; come ye, buy, and eat; yea, come, buy wine and milk without money and without price.

Wherefore do ye spend money for that which is not bread? and your labour for that which satisfieth not? hearken diligently unto me, and eat ye that which is good, and let your soul delight itself in fatness.

Incline your ear, and come unto me: hear, and your soul shall live; and I will make an everlasting covenant with you, even the sure mercies of David.

All that the Father giveth me shall come to me: and him that cometh to me I will in no wise cast out.

For I came down from heaven, not to do mine own will, but the will of him that sent me.

And this is the will of him that sent me, that every one which seeth the Son, and believeth on him, may have everlasting life: and I will raise him up at the last day.

John 3: 14-21; 20: 31

And as Moses lifted up the serpent in the wilderness, even so must the Son of man be lifted up:

That whosoever believeth in him should not perish, but have eternal life.

For God so loved the world, that he gave his only begotten Son, that whosoever believeth in him should not perish, but have everlasting life.

For God sent not his Son into the world to condemn the world; but that the world through him might be saved.

He that believeth on him is not condemned: but he that believeth not is condemned already, because he hath not believed in the name of the only begotten Son of God.

And this is the condemnation, that light is come into the world, and men loved darkness rather than light, because their deeds were evil.

For every one that doeth evil hateth the light, neither cometh to the light, lest his deeds should be reproved.

But he that doeth truth cometh to the light, that his deeds may be made manifest, that they are wrought in God.

These are written, that ye might believe that Jesus is the Christ, the Son of God;

And that believing ye might have life through his name.

John 14: 16-17, 26; 16: 7-14   *Matthew 6: 9-15; 7: 7-11; James 5: 16b*

And I will pray the Father, and he shall give you another Comforter, that he may abide with you for ever;

Even the Spirit of truth; whom the world cannot receive, because it seeth him not, neither knoweth him: but ye know him: for he dwelleth with you, and shall be in you.

But the Comforter, which is the Holy Ghost, whom the Father will send in my name, he shall teach you all things, and bring all things to your remembrance, whatsoever I have said unto you.

Nevertheless I tell you the truth; It is expedient for you that I go away: for if I go not away, the Comforter will not come unto you; but if I depart, I will send him unto you.

And when he is come, he will reprove the world of sin, and of righteousness, and of judgment:

Of sin, because they believe not on me;

Of righteousness, because I go to my Father, and ye see me no more;

Of judgment, because t h e prince of this world is judged.

I have yet many things to say unto you, but ye cannot bear them now.

Howbeit when he, the Spirit of truth, is come, he will guide you into all truth: for he shall not speak of himself; but whatsoever he shall hear, that shall he speak: and he will shew you things to come.

He shall glorify me: for he shall receive of mine, and shall shew it unto you.

After this manner therefore pray ye: Our Father which art in heaven, Hallowed be thy name.

Thy kingdom come. Thy will be done in earth, as it is in heaven.

Give us this day our daily bread.

And forgive us our debts, as ye forgive our debtors.

And lead us not into temptation, but deliver us from evil: For thine is the kingdom. and the power, and the glory, for ever. Amen.

For if ye forgive men their trespasses, your heavenly Father will also forgive you:

But if ye forgive not men their trespasses, neither will your Father forgive your trespasses.

Ask, and it shall be given you; seek, and ye shall find; knock, and it shall be opened unto you:

For every one that asketh receiveth; and he that seeketh findeth; and to him that knocketh it shall be opened.

Or what man is there of you, whom if his son ask bread, will he give him a stone? Or if he ask a fish, will he give him a serpent?

If ye then, being evil, know how to give good gifts unto your children, how much more shall your Father which is in heaven give good things to them that ask him?

The effectual fervent prayer of a righteous man availeth much.

Exodus 20: 3-5a, 7-8, 12-17; · *Matthew 22: 36-39*

Thou shalt have no other gods before me.

Thou shalt not make unto thee any graven image, or any likeness of any thing that is in heaven above, or that is in the earth beneath, or that is in the water under the earth: Thou shalt not bow down thyself to them, nor serve them:

Thou shalt not take the name of the Lord thy God in vain; for the Lord will not hold him guiltless that taketh his name in vain.

Remember the sabbath day, to keep it holy.

Honour thy father and thy mother: that thy days may be long upon the land which the Lord thy God giveth thee.

Thou shalt not kill.

Thou shalt not commit adultery.

Thou shalt not steal.

Thou shalt not bear false witness against thy neighbour.

Thou shalt not covet.

Master, which is the great commandment in the law?

Jesus said unto him, Thou shalt love the Lord thy God with all thy heart, and with all thy soul, and with all thy mind.

This is the first and great commandment.

And the second is like unto it, Thou shalt love thy neighbour as thyself.

Matthew · 24: 45-47; Luke 16: 10-13; .Revelation 2: 10b; I Corinthians 15: 57-58

Who then is a faithful and wise servant, whom his lord hath made ruler over his household, to give them meat in due season?

Blessed is that servant, whom his lord when he cometh shall find so doing.

Verily I say unto you, That he shall make him ruler over all his goods.

He that is faithful in that which is least is faithful also in much: and he that is unjust in the least is unjust also in much.

If therefore ye have not been faithful in the unrighteous mammon, who will commit to your trust the true riches?

And if ye have not been faithful in that which is another man's, who shall give you that which is your own?

No servant can serve two masters: for either he will hate the one, and love the other; or else he will hold to the one, and despise the other. Ye cannot serve God and mammon.

Be thou faithful unto death, and I will give thee a crown of life.

Thanks be to God, which giveth us the victory through our Lord Jesus Christ.

Therefore, my beloved brethren, be ye stedfast, unmovable,· always abounding in the work of the Lord, forasmuch as ye know that your labour is not in vain in the Lord.

Psalms 41: 1-3; Mark 12: 41-44; II Corinthians 8: 1-5

Blessed is he that considereth the poor: the Lord will deliver him in time of trouble.

The Lord will preserve him, and keep him alive; and he shall be blessed upon the earth: and thou wilt not deliver him unto the will of his enemies.

The Lord will strengthen him upon the bed of languishing: thou wilt make all his bed in his sickness.

And Jesus sat over against the treasury, and beheld how the people cast money into the treasury: and many that were rich cast in much.

And there came a certain poor widow, and she threw in two mites, which make a farthing.

And he called unto him his disciples, and saith unto them, Verily I say unto you, That this poor widow hath cast more in, than all they which have cast into the treasury:

For all they did cast in of their abundance; but she of her want did cast in all that she had, even all her living.

Moreover, brethren, we do you to wit of the grace of God bestowed on the churches of Macedonia;

How that in a great trial of affliction the abundance of their joy and their deep poverty abounded unto the riches of their liberality.

For to their power, I bear record, yea, and beyond their power they were willing of themselves;

Praying us with much intreaty that we would receive the gift, and take upon us the fellowship of the ministering to the saints.

And this they did, not as we hoped, but first gave their own selves to the Lord, and unto us by the will of God.

256 Missions

Mark 16: 15; Romans 10: 8-15

And he said unto them, Go ye into all the world, and preach the gospel to every creature.

But what saith it? The word is nigh thee, even in thy mouth, and in thy heart: that is, the word of faith, which we preach;

That if thou shalt confess with thy mouth the Lord Jesus, and shalt believe in thine heart that God hath raised him from the dead, thou shalt be saved.

For with the heart man believeth unto righteousness; and with the mouth confession is made unto salvation.

For the scripture saith, Whosoever believeth on him shall not be ashamed.

For there is no difference between the Jew and the Greek: for the same Lord over all is rich unto all that call upon him.

For whosoever shall call upon the name of the Lord shall be saved.

How then shall they call on him in whom they have not believed? and how shall they believe in him of whom they have not heard?

And how shall they hear without a preacher?

And how shall they preach, except they be sent?

Now faith is the substance of things hoped for, the evidence of things not seen.

By faith Abel offered unto God a more excellent sacrifice than Cain, by which he obtained witness that he was righteous, God testifying of his gifts: and by it he being dead yet speaketh.

By faith Enoch was translated that he should not see death; and was not found, because God had translated him: for before his translation he had this testimony, that he pleased God.

But without faith it is impossible to please him: for he that cometh to God must believe that he is, and that he is a rewarder of them that diligently seek him.

By faith Noah, being warned of God of things not seen as yet, moved with fear, prepared an ark to the saving of his house; by the which he condemned the world, and became heir of the righteousness which is by faith.

By faith Abraham, when he was called to go out into a place which he should after receive for an inheritance, obeyed; and he went out, not knowing whither he went.

By faith he sojourned in the land of promise, as in a strange country, dwelling in tabernacles with Isaac and Jacob, the heirs with him of the same promise:

For he looked for a city which hath foundations, whose builder and maker is God.

Though I speak with the tongues of men and of angels, and have not charity, I am become as sounding brass, or a tinkling cymbal.

And though I have the gift of prophecy, and understand all mysteries, and all knowledge; and though I have all faith, so that I could remove mountains, and have not charity, I am nothing.

And though I bestow all my goods to feed the poor, and though I give my body to be burned, and have not charity, it profiteth me nothing.

Charity suffereth long, and is kind; charity envieth not; charity vaunteth not itself, is not puffed up,

Doth not behave itself unseemly, seeketh not her own, is not easily provoked, thinketh no evil;

Rejoiceth not in iniquity, but rejoiceth in the truth;

Beareth all things, believeth all things, hopeth all things, endureth all things.

Charity never faileth: b u t whether there be prophecies, they shall fail; whether there be tongues, they shall cease; whether there be knowledge, it shall vanish away.

For we know in part, and we prophesy in part. But when that which is perfect is come, then that which is in part shall be done away.

When I was a child, I spake as a child, I understood as a child, I thought as a child: but when I became a man, I put away childish things.

For now we see through a glass darkly; but then face to face: now I know in part; but then shall I know even as also I am known.

Blessed are the poor in spirit: for theirs is the kingdom of heaven.

Blessed are they that mourn: for they shall be comforted.

Blessed are the meek: for they shall inherit the earth.

Blessed are they which do hunger and thirst after righteousness: for they shall be filled.

Blessed are the merciful: for they shall obtain mercy.

Blessed are the pure in heart for they shall see God.

Blessed are the peacemakers: for they shall be called the children of God.

Blessed are they which are persecuted for righteousness' sake: for theirs is the kingdom of heaven.

Blessed are ye, when men shall revile you, and persecute you, and shall say all manner of evil against you falsely, for my sake.

Rejoice, and be exceeding glad: for great is your reward in heaven: for so persecuted they the prophets which were before you.

Ye are the salt of the earth: but if the salt have lost his savour, wherewith shall it be salted? it is thenceforth good for nothing, but to be cast out, and to be trodden under foot of men.

Ye are the light of the world. A city that is set on an hill cannot be hid.

Let your light so shine before men, that they may see your good works, and glorify your Father which is in heaven.

After this I beheld, and, lo, a great multitude, which no man could number, of all nations, and kindreds, and people, and tongues, stood before the throne, and before the Lamb, clothed with white robes, and palms in their hands;

And cried with a loud voice, saying, Salvation to our God which sitteth upon the throne, and unto the Lamb.

And all the angels stood round about the throne, and about the elders and the four beasts, and fell before the throne on their faces, and worshipped God,

Saying, Amen: Blessing, and glory, and wisdom, and thanksgiving, and honour, and power, and might, be unto our God for ever and ever. Amen.

And one of the elders answered, saying unto me, What are these which are arrayed in white robes? and whence came they?

And I said unto him, Sir, thou knowest. And he said to me, These are they which came out of great tribulation, and h a v e washed their robes, and made them white in the blood of the Lamb.

Therefore are they before the throne of God, and serve him day and night in his temple: and he that sitteth on the throne shall dwell among them.

For the Lamb which is in the midst of the throne shall feed them, and shall lead them unto living fountains of waters: and God shall wipe away all tears from their eyes

GENERAL INDEX

GENERAL INDEX

GENERAL INDEX

Index To Responsive Readings

Recitation

"TWENTY-ONE"

Carl Perkins and Jimmie Davis

Twenty-One, Boy, Twenty-One!

Now you were just a young fellow, son, the night your mamma died,
You don't remember it now, but we were right there by mamma's side.
Your ma had this sickness, boy, from all of the work she had done,
And she prayed all of her life that God would let her raise you to be
   twenty-one.

Now me and you never moved to town, boy — we just kept on living out
   here,
And life's been pretty tough, son, for the past twenty-one years.

I remember when you were a young fellow, I used to take you to church,
And to see my boy in the choir with the other children kinda gave old
   dad's heart a jerk.
You sounded like a little angel, boy, and to pa you did look sweet,
Even though your little ragged britches came half way to your skinny
   little knees.
After the services was over, it filled your pa's heart with joy,
When the preacher would pat you on the head and say, "Mr. Brown, you
   sure got a fine little boy."

Then me and you would get in the wagon, boy, and you would look over
   at me and smile,
Then I would hand you the lines and let you drive the team for a while.

Ah, yeah, you and me had a lot of fun and we smiled through a lot of
   tears,
And I wish you could have been a boy for a million years.
But it is so true, son, that time takes its toll,
And that's why boys grow up and men grow old.

Yes, life's been tough for you and me, too, son,
And I have prayed that God would let me raise you to be twenty-one.
But, tonight my life's about over and my work on earth's about done.
Maybe now I will go to see the Lord and live with your mamma,
Because tonight, son, you're TWENTY-ONE!

The Fire Song

Unknown

Arr. by MRS. JAMES A. PATE

1. Oh, the judg-ment day is com-ing; What an aw-ful day 'twill be!
2. At the sound-ing of the trump-et, At the dawning of the day,
3. Poor lost sin-ners will be cry-ing For that home they'll nev-er see,

Christ for-ev-er is my ref-uge, "Rock of A-ges, cleft for me."
World-ly pleas-ures with their treas-ures Shall for-ev-er pass a-way.
But the ran-somed will be sing-ing, "Rock of Ag-es, cleft for me."

CHORUS

Oh, my lov-ing *bro-ther, when the world's on fi-re, Don't you want God's bos-om for to be your pil-low? Hide me o-ver in the Rock of A-ges: "Rock of A-ges, cleft for me."

*May also use "Sister," "Deacon," "Pastor," "Mourner," etc.